AUTOMATED MEDICAL RECORDS AND THE LAW

by Eric W. Springer, LL.B.

THE HEALTH LAW CENTER

Aspen Systems Corporation

4615 Forbes Avenue   Pittsburgh, Pennsylvania 15213

Research for this book was supported in part by
Grant No. HM 00494-01 Department of Health, Education and Welfare

Library of Congress Card #70-110587

PREFACE

This book can trace its beginnings to a paper I delivered at the Annual Meeting of the American Medical Record Association, then called the American Association of Medical Record Librarians in Miami, Florida, in the Fall of 1964. That paper, entitled "Some Legal Implications of Automated Medical Records", primarily raised questions and attempted to point out pitfalls. Later, a series of articles on the subject appeared in "Medical Record News", the Association's journal. Further study was undertaken in collaboration with the Detroit-McComb Hospital pursuant to a grant from the U.S. Department of Health, Education, and Welfare.

In the course of these studies it became quite apparent that despite the tremendous value of computer technology, the law as it is presently structured unduly inhibits the application of computer capabilities to medical record information systems in hospitals and other health care institutions. The law precludes the total replacement of conventional manual systems with computer systems.

It is true that automated systems can be installed at this time, but they must be accompanied by duplicate manual record systems until (a) the automated systems are tested and perfected, (b) the health professions define precisely the kinds of information that will be placed in the computer and (c) the law is modified to reflect the medical and technological changes that have been made.

There is no question that the rapid and continuing experimentation, development and application of techniques, devices, instruments and systems in the health field will benefit and are presently benefiting mankind. In fact, the biomedical explosion provides our nation, at least, with the technological capability to enhance the delivery, quantity and quality of health care. At the very same time we are paradoxically faced with a mounting crisis in health care. The crisis involves a manpower shortage as one of its most important features but there are other factors as well.

The problem we face is as much one of bringing existing technology to the enhancement of the delivery of health care as it is one developing new technology. Much of the needed technology already exists. Much is already on the drawing boards or being tested.

Let me state a prejudice at the outset. I believe that the role of technology in the field of health care must be one of support. This support can take the form of simplifying tasks or passing off existing functions from health care professionals to technicians or machines. The support may provide new and fantastic means for coping with unsolved problems.

But we cannot allow our attraction to machines to blind us to the human equation in health. It is possible, I suppose, to develop instruments and devices which will replace the human relationships in medicine, nursing and the allied health professions. I think we would be foolish to do so. There is growing evidence that we have set upon a course in other areas of industrialization that may lead to significant changes in the delicate balances of nature, as we now know them. I am referring to our current awareness of the effects of air and water pollution, soil destruction, thermal and pesticide pollution, and the destruction of our open spaces all in the name of progress. It is important to understand that this waste and destruction has come about primarily as a result of technological advances which have enhanced a portion of our lives, and we have been dazzled by those advances to such an extent that we could not or would not see the dangerous side effects. I hope that as the new technology modifies medicine and health we will not lack the foresight and strength to build in safeguards and protective measures.

The law is something of an impediment to the use of the new technology. Yet computers for example can presently be employed to provide important supports to the health institution.

Where can the computer be used? Well certainly it can aid in the administrative offices. Management systems can be developed which will give precise and accurate information to administrative personnel on an hourly basis, if necessary. Again on the administrative side of the hospital, billing information, inventory information, purchasing and the like can be converted to automated systems with very handsome results.

In the medical records department, there are many present advantages to the use of computers in processing statistical data and in developing utilization reports, among other things.

In the medical and surgical side, computers can enhance the actual treatment of patients by use of monitoring machines as well as others which could go so far as to replace organs and body parts with mechanical devices.

In the pharmacy, computers and automated delivery systems could reduce the work of the pharmacy and the time required to deliver drugs at the patient's bedside to the point where there could truly be a push-button operation.

In the laboratories, new automated medical testing devices and laboratories would provide large amounts of patient data at low cost.

In laundry, maintenance and housekeeping, computer applications would enhance the efficiency of the hospital. In dietary, again automated kitchens and food delivery systems could prove a boon both in terms of cost and in terms of time. Each of these areas requires an in-depth study.

The prime focus of this book is the medical record. In writing this book I have had support from many sources and individuals. I especially want to acknowledge the American Medical Record Association, and Mrs. Mary J. Waterstraat and Miss Elizabeth Price. A former student, Mr. Saad Ibraham, supplied many thoughtful ideas on technical data processing matters which have found their way into this work. My colleagues at the Health Law Center division of Aspen Systems Corporation, and the availability of its legal information retrieval systems have been most helpful.

All in all this effort was most rewarding to me and I hope it will provide some guidance and assistance to the reader.

Eric W. Springer
September, 1970

ACKNOWLEDGMENT

In addition to the acknowledgments provided by Mr. Springer, the publisher wishes to especially recognize the specific contributions made to this work by Drs. G. Octo Barnett, Rein Turn and Harold E. Petersen.

Much of the material contained in Chapter 1, "Automation and Medicine System Needs and Requirements," is the product of Dr. Barnett, who as Director of the Harvard Medical School's Laboratory of Computer Science authored the "1966 Status Report of The Hospital Computer Project of the Massachusetts General Hospital."

The Health Law Center thanks Drs. Petersen and Turn for permission to use the material which appeared first in the AFIPS Conference Proceedings of the 1967 Spring Joint Computer Conference for our chapter entitled "Safeguards and Protective Measures," pages 72-86.

INTRODUCTION

AUTOMATION AND MEDICINE
SYSTEM NEEDS AND REQUIREMENTS

LEGAL IMPEDIMENTS

CONFIDENTIALITY

SAFEGUARDS AND PROTECTIVE MEASURES

LIABILITIES

THE MEDICAL RECORD IN COURT

BRINGING ABOUT CHANGE

INTRODUCTION

In its short lifetime the computer has had an impact on our society that is nothing less than phenomenal. In government, business, education, travel, entertainment,—in all aspects of our national life the computer is significant. It processes our checks, keeps our inventories and guides astronauts to the moon. It performs all kinds of jobs mundane and magnificent.

Electronic technology, of which computer technology is part, will be of enormous aid in health care. Not only will the new devices and instruments and the techniques they spawn enhance our ability to deal with current disease and illness, but we will have the capability to assimilate more and more knowledge and experience about health problems and thereby develop cures and remedies. The emerging specialties in medicine and its allied professions and skills may allow us to employ more people in the continuing battle against sickness. Computers will play a large role in this battle.

One area in which the computer is recognized as having a great potential is in the processing of information about patients. As the report of the panel on the impact of new technologies of the National Advisory Commission on Health Manpower stated:

> The panel believes that there is an urgent need for an improved capability to provide medical records for the patient. We are persuaded that the advances in modern data processing and communications provide a feasible and perhaps unique solution for this problem in the form of a patient data bank. We see such a data bank as an accumulation of individual medical history and data, promptly accessible, in toto or selectively, to authorized physicians at the point of care. The patient data bank would receive information from physicians, hospitals, and testing laboratories via telephone lines acting as transmission links. The input and output from the data bank can be either graphical (x-rays) or in familiar typed form. Such a data bank should yield medical records both more complete and more readily available than has ever been the case.

> The patient data bank should allow a much more sensitive characterization of the state of the individual in comparison with his own normal status as well as in comparison with the population average, from which the individual may depart substantially and consistently. But it can also furnish selective summaries for emergency care. The information in the

1

data bank can be safeguarded by reliable techniques so that it is available only upon authorization by the individual. In fact, with technological, organizational, and legal safeguards, information would be more secure in this system than in the present form as a written record. Nevertheless, such information could still be made available, without identification of the individual, to support research and epidemiology, distribution of the test results, large-scale indices of health, etc., without compromise of privacy. Such analyses could establish wide data-base norms and more accurately determine the significance of deviations from the norms, the meaning of trends and distribution, and the significance of correlations between volumes and changes in various measurements. The number and location of data banks will be a compromise between communication costs and economics of large-scale storage and processing. The panel believes that such computerized patient data banks are essential to an efficient health care program.

The panel recommends that a central patient data bank be implemented, with adequate safeguards, at an early date on an experimental basis within the complex of federally operated hospitals, and that planning be carried out for a national system.[1]

The need for medical record information is changing rapidly and dramatically. This is due in part to the impact of new technology and new health delivery systems. There was a time—not too long ago—when the emphasis in medical record management was upon protection against disclosure. The administrator and medical record librarian stood firm against any and all attacks and forays by "intruders". Everyone was suspect, even members of the governing board.[2] Today, because of changing technology and changing notions of the ways in which health care should be delivered, the information in the medical record is to be disseminated to a wide variety of authorized individuals. The emphasis has switched from protection to information flow.

The medical record remains the principal communication device among the individuals who provide care directly to the patient. But the number of individuals has increased.

The medical record is the information repository for purposes of evaluation of care rendered.

The medical record is the tool for the review of utilization of health facilities, medical care and services, in their broadest definitions.[3]

The medical record provides information for purposes of defining costs, providing reimbursement data, and developing rates of payment.

The medical record provides information for purposes of continuing care in institutions other than hospitals.

The medical record provides information for the generation of statistics, for research, for education and for training.

The medical record provides information about the quality of care being provided in the institution.

Information flow and utilization are the concerns today. The medical record is or should be the repository of that information and the starting point of that flow.

At the least an automated medical record system should:

1. Increase the speed and accuracy of collecting, recording, transmitting, retrieving and summarizing patient care information;

2. Decrease the amount of routine paper work required of the nursing and allied staffs;

3. Arrange and consolidate information for more effective and efficient utilization by the medical staff;

4. Store large amounts of complex medical information and contribute to research by facilitating rapid and efficient manipulation, analysis and retrieval of stored information.

The general theme of this book is that computers should be employed to aid in the efficient and rapid collection, analysis and dissemination of medical record data. But the present state of the law is a restrictive barrier to the application of computer technology to medical records. It is the purpose of this book to point out the problems and the pitfalls and to suggest methods for change. It is first necessary to define some legal terms and concepts.

Section 1
The Nature of Law

While there is no distinct body of law relating specifically to medical records as such, there are a number of laws and regulations which affect the development of automated medical record information systems.

It is generally the case that the law—taking that to mean the entire disparate collection of rules and controls reflected in judicial opinions, statutes and regulations—operates after the fact. Government makes laws in response to existing influences; government generally does not anticipate new human activity; it reacts after questions, problems or situations have been created. Our statutes, regulations and judicial decisions attempt to create guidelines for the solutions of problems that already exist. Admittedly it is not always true that the best solutions are initially selected, but the law can be modified as we gain experience.

At times the law may attempt to solve imaginary problems. A good example of this is the so-called Good Samaritan Law which has been adopted by a majority of the states and which purports to protect physicians, nurses and other health professionals from liability when they render assistance in disaster or emergency situations. It was discovered after careful research that there were no reported cases or claims against physicians or others arising out of such accident situations. The wrong that the statute purported to protect against was an imaginary one. Yet laws were written and enacted by many state legislatures. The point here is that the law can be used to achieve a variety of ends. It can be changed, but those who seek change should be clear about the nature of the change required.

Moreover, even though we say that the legal system generates specific rules and guidelines, more often than not the rules are quite general. We have to apply those general pronouncements to specific sets of facts. Our judicial, statutory and administrative systems of law making are organized this way. Nevertheless, the law is used as a guide to future action because we predict a course of conduct based on the rules we find presently to exist. Until it can be demonstrated that existing law is inapplicable or until new legal standards are shown to be needed, the law as it exists will be the determining guide for resolution of problems which appear when we attempt to inaugurate new activities. In short, the law is the law—good, bad or indifferent.

The subject of this book is a prime example of what has been said. We are here attempting to determine how existing law, created generally without reference to automation, affects the application of the techniques of automation to medical recordation.

It should be clear at the outset that the legal materials analyzed here have been promulgated with few exceptions to meet problems other than automation. Nevertheless, existing laws, regulations and cases affect the development of automated medical record information systems. And because they affect such development they have to be identified, understood and dealt with, that is, amended, repealed, or reinterpreted. Until they are so changed, these rules, regulations and decisions remain the law applicable to the question of automated medical record information systems.

Each source of law, the legislative, executive and judicial, will affect the way in which we solve problems. It is not meant to imply that the activ-

4

ities of government are coordinated. Indeed, it is most likely that each branch of government will act independently of the other. The pronouncements may be in conflict.

For the purpose of this writing it is enough to remind the reader that there are two systems of government in the United States. The federal government is one of "limited" powers which are found in the Constitution as it has been amended and interpreted. The state governments have broad powers which are limited to some degree primarily by the Fourteenth Amendment to the United States Constitution. In matters of health the states' powers are very broad.

Both the federal and state governments are divided into three main branches: The executive, the judicial, and the legislative. Each of these branches produce requirements which form part of the law.

The executive branch of government produces law through the regulations of administrative departments and agencies. The legislative branch produces law by means of statutes it is empowered to enact. The judicial branch of government produces law by means of its case decisions which adjudicate disputes between contesting parties and the interpretation of statutes.

Both the federal and state governments have the power to deal with health matters. The federal government's powers are limited to those which have been granted to it by the Constitution as it has been interpreted and amended over the years. The power to deal with matters of public health is one of the primary attributes of government. It is called the police power. It means much more than the right to issue a traffic ticket. The state's police power is very broad. It is the power to act to promote and protect the health, safety, welfare and morals of the community. The police power is particularly applicable in the field of health. Under the police power the legislature may delegate to political subdivisions, such as counties, and to administrative agencies, such as boards of health or licensing agencies, the authority and power to control, regulate, define, authorize or prohibit all activities in the field of public health.

The requirement that medical records be kept is found primarily in regulations which have been promulgated by licensing agencies and boards. Protection of the confidentiality of information is found in statutes primarily. The judicial branch of government, through court cases provides the precedents relating to liability, ownership, and disclosure of medical records. Thus all three branches of government have contributed to the law of medical records. These regulations set forth minimum record requirements.

Section 2
Results of the Study

This book reports on the present state of the law as it affects medical record automation according to these broad considerations.

1. The creation and maintenance of records
2. The disclosure of information from records
3. Liability for mishandling of records

These general subject areas all relate to the principal requirements of a medical record system: security and reliability.

It should be noted that system security and system reliability are independent and equally forceful requirements for any information system. That is, the most secure and protected system is actually worth little if the information is unreliable or inaccurate. By the same token, the worth of the most accurate and reliable system is diminished if there are inadequate protections against unwarranted disclosure, whether intentional or unintentional. This is so with any information system, it is particularly so with reference to a medical record information system where the concept of confidentiality is such a major governing factor.

Undoubtedly, as automated devices are used in the hospital more information will be generated. It will be used by more individuals who have a legitimate need to receive and analyze it. System reliability will assume an even greater importance while system security may diminish in importance at least insofar as our present notions of confidentiality are concerned. Nevertheless, the competing needs of confidentiality and disclosure will be with us for some time to come.

System security and system reliability are concerns to be recognized and accommodated because they are manifested in the way the laws are written. As we shall see records must be authenticated by signatures and they must be protected because of confidentiality.

The specific findings of this study of the legal aspects of automated medical record information systems can be summarized as follows:

1. There is no discrete body of medical records law as such. The legal materials affecting the development of an automated medical record information system are found in statutes and regulations and in some decisions dealing with various questions of law.

2. The present posture of the law precludes the creation of an automated system which would totally replace conventional manual systems. At the present time, not only must the law of each state be analyzed before a system is inaugurated, but, strategies and procedures must be developed for changing existing laws and regulations so that they will reflect the advantage and potential of automation and technological advance.

3. Automated medical record systems can be installed and used at the

6

present time (assuming operational feasibility), but manual records will have to be kept until the systems are perfected and can be measured by standards yet to be developed, and until the statutes, regulations and judicial guidelines are modified to enhance and authorize technological potential.

4. A machine system, to some degree, will offer better protections and safeguards and ensure higher levels of system security and system reliability because of its built-in capability to check, question and require verification of the information it receives. However, no new electronic system offers any more protection than presently available manual systems if the information is not input correctly or not used correctly by humans whose job it is to read and make decisions or follow instructions. Moreover, human error is not absolutely prevented or preventable by the introduction of automated data processing techniques. In fact, the possibility of error may be increased, despite the fact of built-in checks, precisely because automation introduces new and complicated techniques of information input, storage processing and retrieval. Thus, the general rules of law relating to negligence (essentially the lack of care which results in harm to another person) apply to automated medical record information systems with reference to those who create the system, those who operate it, those who supply it with information and those who use its output. The user moreover, must always be aware of his continuing responsibility to check the output of the system.

5. Information stored in automated systems can be retrieved and admitted as evidence in judicial and quasi-judicial proceedings so long as a proper foundation for such admission is laid by the custodian of the record, the supervisor of the data processing unit or an individual in a position of authority who can lay such a foundation. The testimony should include a full description of the way in which the medical information is obtained, placed in machine readable form, stored, retrieved, used and safeguarded.

6. Automated medical record systems will require that the medical, nursing and allied health professions develop uniform terminology and standards of measurement, if a system is to achieve its highest potential for the enhancement of the *quality and quantity* of medical care.

It is with this understanding of the new demands upon the medical record that this book will review the way in which the law affects the application of computer technology to the record. It is important to understand the impact of these new demands upon the medical record despite the fact that a health institution may not presently contemplate the acquisition of computer capability or the application of its computer to medical records.

In a sense, this book explores the manner in which the law affects technological progress in the health field generally, as well as the specific application of law to existing medical record systems.

We will look at the basic legal considerations in the application of automation to medical record keeping and how changes in the law can be implemented. A state-by-state analysis of statutes, regulations and judicial decisions will close the book.

FOOTNOTES

[1] Report of the National Advisory Commission on Health Manpower, Vol. II, Nov. 1967.

[2] In Hyman v. Jewish Chronic Disease Hospital, 15 N.Y.2d 317, 258 N.Y.S.2d 397 (N.Y., 1965), the Court of Appeals of N.Y. held that a member of a hospital's governing board was entitled to inspect the medical records of the hospital so that he could investigate alleged illegal and improper experimentation on patients. The court stated that the confidentiality of hospital records could be amply protected. In dismissing the contention of the administrator that medical records must be kept absolutely confidential, even with respect to a member of the governing board, the court said that all kinds of qualified persons, staff members and employees see, read and copy such medical records. A governing board member has a duty to protect the hospital corporation and he, too, is a qualified person.

[3] Note should be made of the excellent discussion of the definitions of "medical care" and "medical services" found in the *Glossary of Hospital Terms,* American Association of Medical Record Librarians, Chicago, 1969.

AUTOMATION AND MEDICINE

Advances in biomedical research and development and the consequent production of devices which are marketed commercially continue with a rapidity which is astounding even to the most optimistic person. We are all familiar with at least some of the innovations. Perhaps the best known devices are the electromechanical replacements for human body parts, such as implantable cardiac pace makers and mechanized prosthetic devices. Another application is the instrumentation for automating laboratory procedures and those related to the automatic monitoring of a patient's physical condition.

While the majority of hospitals do not yet have monitoring devices, all of the larger hospitals have some automated laboratory procedures and devices. As time goes on more hospitals will acquire these and other kinds of equipment. When this happens hospital and medical practice will have to change to take full advantage of the potential of these devices, instruments and techniques.

When we speak of change we mean substantive as well as procedural change. And it is not necessarily true that all the changes resulting from increased use of computers in health will be good. For example, reliance on automated tests results may lead to a *diminution* rather than an enhancement of the physician's skill in diagnosis and treatment.

One implication, then, of the application of computers to the hospital relates to the area of medical and professional practice. It is only partially facetious to say that we may be approaching the time when the computer or other electronic device will practice medicine, nursing, or pharmacy. Indeed, in the pharmacy, it is now possible to formulate a totally automated department, requiring no human intervention. Think for a moment, if you will, of the ability of present systems to call up the required amount of chemicals, mix them in the proper proportions, put them on conveyors and dispense them to a patient's bedside. Suppose a machine could be developed to administer certain kinds of medications; that step would begin to replace one traditional function of the physician and the nurse.

Again, focusing on the physician, it is possible, at some point in time, for the machine to instruct the physician on the proper course to follow. If the machine were given sufficient hard medical data, it could postulate a diagnosis and develop a set of recommended procedures in priority and it could, it seems, provide specific guidelines for the work to be performed. In this hypothetical situation, the physician would be an appendage of the machine rather than vice versa. It has already been indicated that it is techno-

11

logically possible to usurp the compounding and dispensing arts of the pharmacists; we can limit severely some practices of the nurse and we can modify extremely the doctor's art and science. It is the case that the physician is the person we depend upon to make the medical judgments which lead to medical treatment. Certainly we depend upon his skillful manipulation of instruments when he performs surgery. But long before surgery is performed the physician must apply his "art and science" to make the determination that surgery is in fact required. Moreover, he and his human consultants must decide the nature of the procedure and how it is to be performed.

Again, our ability to store, handle and retrieve large amounts of information, goes to the core of our notions of privacy. Do the physician's, clergyman's, nurse's, lawyer's, psychologist's and medical record librarian's obligations of secrecy cease once they fill out a record card? Assuming the answer is "no", how will they meet this obligation in the computerized future? Think of the computer as a non moral collection of responsive electronic gadgets. It may or may not be discreet. It can and will act as a servant or as a master. We merely have to give it an instruction. More to the point, our present promises and protections may give way to future pressures.

The fine print on the early Social Security Card contained language which declared "For social security purposes only—not to be used for identification." When the Social Security program was created the Congress was concerned that people might be branded with numbers. To meet this objection, assurance was given that Social Security numbers would never be used for any purposes other than identification of an individual's Social Security record. Today it is a rare personal record form, whether from a department store, credit card agency or the Internal Revenue Service, that does not ask for this information. As time moves on, original intent becomes modified to meet new needs in the name of efficiency.

Future changes in record keeping must be anticipated. This is not only today's problem, but tomorrow's as well. Today, from the viewpoint of the data processor, we are still in the quill pen stage of medical record keeping. The physician's sensitive office records are kept in a file probably with the drawers half-opened. The medical record room in the hospital is in a perpetual turmoil over misplaced, incomplete, subpoenaed, and requisitioned records. The impact of new technology has not yet been fully felt. But, it is coming. It is important to anticipate the future and face the issues as we seek to acquire the full benefits of the tremendous improvements possible in automated information systems. These systems offer so many obvious advantages over manual record keeping in both cost and performance that their advent in this field is guaranteed.

A summary of the major changes expected during the next decade in information automation will indicate the nature of possible problems.

1. A rapid expansion in time-shared computer file systems is expected. We will have centralized computers feeding a large number of remotely connected consoles such as those used today for making and checking airline reservations. Information will be stored into the computer and any portions of it can be retrieved and recombined in any manner we wish. The cost for this form of record keeping will eventually be less than our present manual methods and access will be better.

2. This new computational and storage service may be provided like a utility. Physicians, for example, may purchase computer time and file storage like electricity—from a utility. They will pay for the amount they use.

3. There will be constant economic pressure inherent in the "utility" nature of these future information systems to centralize them by interconnecting them for reasons of both economy and performance. It is in this eventual fully interconnected era where under-designed systems could become most embarrassing—and, in some instances, downright dangerous to our present concepts of a right to privacy. But, at the same time, we must acknowledge that such interconnected systems will make large files readily accessible and permit better research using statistical sample sizes that would be economically infeasible today. Thus, we will have to achieve a balance. How do we obtain the greatest benefit with the least danger?

Just as this new body of data may be searched for socially beneficial purposes, we must also consider the ease with which files could be illicitly searched for derogatory information. To be most beneficial, the new file systems must allow inquiry from a large number of geographically scattered points. It should be realized, however, that the communications network (normally telephone wires) is wide open to tampering.

While the invasion of privacy problem has always been with us, its magnitude and complexion is changing. In the past, personal, sensitive information was kept in separate manual files. Specific individual permission was required any time an outsider wished information. The high cost and nuisance of delving through the files made inquiries by outsiders relatively rare and tightly controlled.

The major changes underway in the financing of medical care can greatly broaden the access of formerly private physician-patient information:

1. The growth of prepaid medical insurance plans.

2. The role of industry in selecting and financing medical, disability and life insurance programs as a fringe benefit. Preventive medicine is now regarded as a proper concern of a corporate personnel department.

3. Population increase and mobility requires more widespread transfer of medical information.

4. Increased specialization in medicine requires more complex and subdivided diagnostic centers.

5. More computer on-line patient monitoring in hospitals and automation of tests may be anticipated. These produce larger volumes of records.

6. The payoff for better research by better use of existing personal records is becoming more widely appreciated.

7. Federal and state governments have a heavy involvement in medical care which includes care of the indigent, financing medical research, care of the elderly through Medicare and medicaid as well as comprehensive health planning. Eventually, some form of national health insurance will be enacted which will challenge all of our concepts about medical records.

It has been said that the most important historic event in the growth of the data processing industry was the advent of the Social Security program in the thirties. The vast volume of data that had to be processed could not have been economically handled without data processing techniques. A new technology allowed a new social function to be performed.

As we look to the future and foresee greater need for integrated medical information systems, it is necessary to plan for the orderly development of such systems.

The problems such systems will create are not new; but their magnitude will increase. The change may be so great that a change of *quantity* may well mean a change in the *quality* of life.

A few stories—perhaps apocryphal—which touch upon the weakness of present-day practices, show how easily an automated system can be misused. This will give an indication of the potential problems.

Physicians feel that discussions with patients are private affairs. But with the growing number of company-sponsored group medical programs, some information may spread beyond the privacy of physicians' offices and may be used to the detriment of their patients.

There is the story of a young career woman employed by a benevolent if stuffy, blue-chip company which gave all its key employees free annual medical examinations. During her routine physical examination she mentioned in passing that she had been undergoing psychoanalysis for several years. The woman refused to discuss the matter further but was badgered into accounting all the details because the examining physician insisted that it was impossible for him to complete his medical examination without this information. She was assured that the information would, of course, be kept private. Within two weeks, her immediate supervisor knew of the details and within three, all of her co-workers.

There are other stories. For example, a major electronics company also provides mandatory physical examinations for its top executives. One very competent engineer was tentatively selected to head a new major program. The man's supervisor, reluctant to lose his valuable subordinate, stated that the company's physician had told him that during the previous annual physical examination this man was found to have suffered a minor stroke. Upon checking with the company's legal staff, an opinion was given that if this man were allowed to take the new job with its responsibilities and suffered a heart attack, the company might be liable because it knew of the situation. He did not get the job. The man never knew he was considered and that chances for his advancement were restricted.

Other companies have major medical plans which reimburse the employee for medical and prescription drug bills. However, it is usually necessary to obtain complete statements of all visits to physicians and all pharmaceutical bills, including prescription numbers. These are not filed with the insurance company, but rather with the corporations themselves which in turn forward the claims. Token pretense is made of information privacy by mailing the forms in sealed envelopes.

Social morality differs from one generation to another. We can imagine, at present, situations where a coed might receive contraceptive advice from the student health office. She may not know that a record of her request is carefully recorded along with information about her grades, her sorority, her religion, political activity, and her parents' economic situation. This may seem farfetched, knowing how carefully physicians are supposed to preserve their records from the prying eye of the curious, but we live in a new world where pressures to automate records and make them more widely available are great. The economic and social benefits that more complete records can provide are compelling reasons that can put us on the defensive. Further, we may like to believe that all we will do is to automate a manual procedure that is today satisfactorily secure. But we should move cautiously at this time in response to the inherent weakness and limitations of the technological design of some interconnected systems that are being used and proposed today.

A few years ago, a freshman fascinated by a computer used at a major school of engineering (and possibly in response to the reputation of freshmen to dream up pranks) programmed the computer to dial every telephone extension in the school at the same time. The telephone switchboard operator saw her switchboard light up like a Christmas tree and acted instinctively. Instead of waiting to answer any of the calls, she immediately dialed the fire department.

A freshman prankster could easily be tempted to probe the college's computerized file to find tidbits of information about his friends.

According to a recent survey made by the American College Health Association, approximately 10 percent of the student health services already issue contraceptives to unmarried coeds. The prescription files which contain this information may be computerized in the future. Can we imagine what a freshman (or senior for that matter) might be able to do if he were able to interrogate these files? It would only take little more of the same imagination used in writing a program to ring all of the school's telephones. College students have not been known to exercise the highest degree of discretion.

It may seem bizarre to think about such problems while physicians and hospitals are still writing their records on sheets of 8 1/2 x 11 paper to be stored in locked file cabinets. But it isn't too early to look forward to the day when a sufficient amount of personal and embarrassing information will be found in computers. Hospital records are not the only ones which pose this problem. Those records are merely a portion of the vast amount of information which could describe an individual to his possible disadvantage.

But, remembering that the initial intention with respect to the confidentiality of the Social Security number changed significantly in the interest of efficiency, we must consider the consequences of a similar evolution that can take place during the automation of the physicians' and hospitals' sensitive records.

From the vantage point of our present awareness, what kind of an automated medical record system should be built?

SYSTEM NEEDS AND REQUIREMENTS

This book discussion assumes a totally automated medical record system involving a time-shared, remote-access computer capability. Admittedly, such a total system does not now exist, but the capacity of computers to accommodate the massive amounts of data required in medical recordation is known. Even today applications of computer technology to the processing of clinical and laboratory data have taken place. Many attempts at refinement are in the developmental stage.

Section 1
System Needs

Since this chapter deals with the application of automation to hospital operations, it is best to first identify several minimum system objectives. Any automated medical record system should seek:

1. To increase the rapidity and accuracy of collecting, recording, transmitting, retrieving and summarizing patient care information.

2. To decrease the amount of routine paper work required of the nursing staff.

3. To arrange and consolidate information for more effective and efficient utilization by the medical staff.

Some of the major considerations involved in planning for these objectives are:

1. The collection of historical data from the patient.

2. The utilization of electronic techniques to record and automatically analyze physical phenomena such as the electrocardiogram.

3. The simultaneous processing of numerous laboratory tests on a single patient, with automatic computation analysis and evaluation of the test results.

4. The epidemiological collection and analysis of masses of patient care data in order to classify patterns of disease, medical care and medical needs.

Section 2
The Communications Problem

The problem of information retrieval from the medical record must be considered in close relation to the communication problem in the hospital; that is, the problem of transmitting information as it is being generated.

The clinical investigator who attempts to perform any large-scale study of the occurrence of a disease entity, symptom complex, drug intake, pathological diagnosis or laboratory test, is confronted with the problem of laboriously extracting this data from a large number of relatively unclassified records where the information is scattered over many pages in often illegible script. If the investigator attempts to study the correlation between several different variables, his task becomes so tedious and time-consuming that few workers have the resources to carry out this important type of research.

There are no theoretical or technical reasons why a powerful information storage and retrieval system could not be created by storing, in computer readable form, all or a large subset of, the data which are available in the medical record library. This transition from current methods of information handling however, must be viewed with certain factors in mind, namely:

1. Present manual systems would have to be restructured so that the data are placed in forms which are both efficient for computer assisted analysis and still meaningful for manual processes.

2. Additional staff and commensurate financing would be required for development of such a system.

3. For the entire transition process to be of any real value, a technique for effecting data uniformity and compatability would have to be established.

It is the impression of most clinical investigators that historical research on medical records in their present form is limited considerably by the lack of uniformity in both the method of collection and the definition of terminology. For example, two medical experts on the subject have said:

> "The value of the medical record as a repository for the physician's observations and judgments is unquestionable. However, the data collected are so variable in origin and in relevance to the patient's true situation that the replacing of the medical record has become cumbersome, its actual usage ineffective, and the retrieval of information contained therein difficult if not impossible."[4]

Any comprehensive information system involves four basic stages.

1) data acquisition

2) data conversion to computer readable form

3) data retrieval

4) analysis of retrieved data

In one sense, the practice of medicine and the operation of a hospital can be looked upon as problems of cyclic information processing. The patient-physician interaction, for example, consists of an initial period of data collection; then the formation of some hypothesis concerning the nature of the disease process and the requisition of indicated laboratory tests takes place. After the performance of the tests, the physician evaluates the new evidence and refines or extends the hypothesis. He then institutes appropriate medical or surgical treatment. Each proposed treatment is to some extent an experiment and after it has been carried out, the same cycle repeats: collection of data, reformulation of hypothesis, requisition and evaluation of further tests and continuation or modification of the treatment plan.

Two aspects of this routine are of importance to our discussion:

First, the practice of medicine in the modern hospital now involves the constant interaction of a number of different individuals - professional, technical, and administrative. The case of a single patient may involve not only his personal physician but several consultants, a radiologist, pathologist, anesthesiologist, psychiatrist, numerous nurses, and many laboratory technicians in addition to the administrative staff and the staffs of the pharmacy, social service department, the admitting office, the dietary department and even the housekeeping and maintenance services. Second, significant problems exist in the requisition and collection of the data, the communication between the various individuals and laboratories and the storage retrieval of essential information. For the most part, the present procedures in hospitals involve either oral communication or manipulation of written documents. In numerous situations, the limitations of such methods both as to accuracy, convenience and speed place serious restrictions on the quality and efficiency of medical care.

It is acknowledged that the processes of information collection, storage and retrieval as well as that of communication can and should be restructured and modernized in order to enhance the ability to provide more and better patient care. This is one of many reasons why computers are regarded with such favor. Yet before one can exploit computers to the fullest one must understand the way information is processed.

Section 3
The Information Flow

The flow of information in a hospital is composed of a large number of complex and often poorly-defined procedures. For the most part these procedures were not systematically planned, but rather evolved in a relatively uncoordinated fashion over many decades through attempts to meet separate needs in separate areas of service. The procedures are largely based on manual methods of transcribing information and communication by courier, supplemented by direct telephone messages. The architecture of hospitals, the patterns of administrative responsibilities, and the conventions of patient care were all developed for systems of medical practice quite different from the current needs.

The number of activities concerned with the collection, transmission, storage and retrieval of information in a general hospital is impressive. For example, in such a hospital, the medical records department may be expected to store more than a million records or abstracts in less than twenty years, in addition to other records in branch hospitals, nursing homes or clinics in other locations. During an average day, such a hospital may issue some hundreds of new patient records. Thousands of demands for existing records are made. Actually, at least twenty per-cent of these records cannot be immediately located. Moreover, such a hospital will admit some tens of thousands of patients annually. It will receive additional numbers of patients to be treated in the emergency room and out-patient departments at the rate of approximately five times the number of admitted patients.

During the peak periods of activity, hundreds of patients are in transit within such a hospital. The various laboratories may perform over a million procedures per year. Innumerable telephone calls are commonly made between patient care areas, the laboratories and the various physicians' offices. Every day the laboratory receives hundreds of telephone calls concerning results of laboratory tests. Each time a patient is admitted, pertinent information is sent to many different areas. It is estimated that on an average day, in such a hospital, thousands of doctor's orders are written and the nursing service administers tens of thousands of drugs and treatments. It is probable that some tens of thousands of other separate items of information are entered into patient records each day, or many millions of separate items each year.

The problems created by the large bulk of information processing are greatly magnified by the complexity of the data flow. For example, the many different laboratories in such a general hospital will perform some hundreds of different laboratory tests involved in routine patient care.

Another feature of medical and hospital practice that increases the information problem is the frequent "explosion" of one order into many different written procedures and notifications. One simple order, such as the request for a fasting blood test, requires a list of routines:

1. Written completion of a requisition to the laboratory and notation on the patient's chart.

2. Determination of the type of sample and the amount that is required.

3. Selection and notification of the team to draw the blood.

4. Notification to the dietary department to delay feeding and then to reinstate the feeding schedule after drawing of the test sample.

5. Checking that there is no conflict of orders and that the patient will be available for the collection of the sample.

6. Actual collection of the sample and notation on the patient's chart.

7. Transporting the sample to the appropriate laboratory with the requisition by the message service.

8. Logging in the sample in the laboratory.

9. Scheduling and performing the test analysis by the laboratory technician.

10. Transcribing the test result from the laboratory work sheet to the original test requisition.

11. Filing the information to allow the appropriate charges to be made.

12. Transporting the completed requisition with the test results to the appropriate patient care unit.

13. Sorting all the test results for a given care unit and posting the result in the appropriate patient's medical record.

14. Finally, the physician must find the test result and evaluate its meaning in light of all other information known about the patient.

A third feature of information processing in a hospital that further compounds the problem is the translation that frequently is required between different domains of activity. For example, all physician's orders are written for individual patients (i.e., in the patient domain) and the information about the time the order is to be performed varies widely and is specified by the particular orders. In contrast, the orders implemented by the nursing service represent a different cross-section of the information in that lists must be prepared of drug orders due at particular hours. This means that the information must be transformed from lists in the patient domain (the patient's record) to lists in the time domain (a list of all the orders for a given time for all patients). The manual transformation from the patient domain to the time domain requires many hours of clerical work on the part of the nursing staff. For example, a nurse in each care unit may spend four hours each day on bookkeeping activities concerned with the ordering, administering and recording of medications.

Given the importance of the information constantly flowing in the hospital it is most important to design a system to meet the communication requirements which are inherent in the provision of high quality care. It is not possible, of course, to detail the requirements which any particular hospital may have. It is possible, however, to state the requirements of the system in general terms.

Section 4
System Requirements

Long before a system is installed there must be a thorough evaluation of needs and objectives. Once these are established, the next step is the specification and design of the system components. Included here are both the "hardware," the physical components, and the "software," the computer programs and procedural components.

The information system in its final form will consist of a series of "application programs," those programs designed specifically for user application to information processing needs, as opposed to programs which control the operation of the computer itself, so-called operating system programs.[5]

In developing specifications for application programs, it must be understood that simulation of present forms of hospital reporting may cause significant loss of efficiency and therefore raise the cost of operation. Conversely, however, over-emphasizing the computer in those areas where the system interacts with the human users may cause adverse reaction by the users—they will not readily accept the system since it would appear more as an imposition than a useful new tool. The task of the systems designers, then, is one of balancing considerations of system efficiency against the need of keeping the system as transparent to the users as possible.

The failure of many contemporary systems can be traced to unyielding or naive systems designers who have designed system capabilities without proper consideration of human engineering aspects. Likewise, other unsuccessful implementations were the result of indulgence to user whims without consideration of processing costs in complex system environments.

Neither medical personnel nor the systems designers alone can develop a hospital computer system; there must be close interaction in every step of the process. The specification procedures will require a considerable period of intense collaboration between the systems analysts, programmers and the responsible individuals on the hospital staff. The individuals who have had sufficient experience with hospital operation in order to understand the content area generally have little practice in describing a procedure in precise details. Yet the many facets and explanations of *why* procedures are done in a certain way can only be understood by one who has had extensive experience observing and participating in actual hospital functioning. The delineation of information processing in a hospital cannot be easily undertaken by an outside consultant.

Even the design of the file structure, though the structure will be completely internal, is an area in which the hospital and programming staffs must work closely together. The programmers must make the decisions about such items as the nature of the scheduling files and the time-course of the flow of information into and out of the files. But these decisions must be made in the context of full knowledge of the constraints of actual hospital operation and cannot be based on artificial assumptions, however logical they might appear. The project has to realize the full implications of what has been described as "program-drift".

"Unfortunately, when a computer based system is being planned there are many unknowns, especially connected with programming. When eventually a program is being done, many justifiable decisions may have been taken by the programmers which cause the system to drift away from the original design concepts. It has commonly been the experience on complex computer based systems that a large drift away from the original design has been experienced when a system is being implemented. This drift can have catastrophic results. An expenditure which cannot be justified is needed to put matters right, or else the programming must be thought out fresh, which may delay the implementation of the system by a year or more."[6]

23

Since most of the following discussion refers specifically to a systems organization known as an "on-line" or interactive mode of operation it is worthwhile to become familiar with some basic terminology and, at the same time, the alternatives in user-computer communication.

There are two basic operational categories between which distinctions may be made in planning for systems requirements, they are "on-line" and "batch processing."

In "batch processing" a program is loaded into the computer memory and it processes several unrelated jobs sequentially. A typical operation of this type is the tabulation of the hospital payroll by processing each employee's record individually in one continuous operation.

"On-line" refers to an operational mode and types of devices capable of maintaining continuous dialogue between the user and the computer. An increasingly common example of this type of equipment is the cathode ray tube - keyboard console. It is essentially a TV screen on which data may be displayed. It will permit the user to process information nearly simultaneously with the computer, receiving almost immediate response to his inquiries and processing requirements.

In the "batch processing" mode of operation, the user is, in most cases, physically divorced from the computer's response, usually leaving his job with a computer operator to be processed overnight.

Within the general category of "on-line" lies a term called "conversational mode." This refers to an on-line system which allows the user to begin his search for information by participating in a series of queries and responses which will guide him to the most relevant data in an efficient and timely manner. A typical example of this is the "error message" which is received on the user's terminal indicating that he is following incorrect procedures to query the system.

It is beyond the purview of this book to delve into the factors which make either "batch processing" or "on-line" interaction the most cost-effective system.

Interaction between various programs will create an additional problem in specification. In many cases, several programs will add data to the same file; therefore, each program may interact with several other programs. It is important that the function under study be considered in its entirety, and that one individual have responsibility for coordinating the specification development, working with one programmer who must have responsibility for coordinating the coding of the various routines.

In specifying programs, we may encounter certain conflicts which would require a variety of compromises. For example, as mentioned previously, the program will be used by operators with varying degrees of experience; ideally the style of the program should exactly match the operator's needs. This problem can be partially solved by creating the capability to

24

ask long or short types of computer questions, and providing a "HOW" reply that is detailed.[7]

Another kind of conflict will concern the amount of information returned in the error messages where the experienced operator will require only minimal detail but the beginning operator will require considerable specification.

A similar conflict may occur because of the difference in appearance and operation between the programs that will be used for teaching and training and the programs that will be used for actual operations. A teaching program should have an expansive feed-back capability. But an operational program should be geared for producing results which do not inhibit the delivery of care. In other words it is important to have a built-in elaborate query-response capability for training purposes but not for actual operation. For example, a user of a Medication Order Program may be informed by the computer that a certain drug which was just ordered should not be used in the presence of liver disease. When this feed-back first occurs, the user will be very impressed; however, by the tenth time it happens he may be annoyed, and when it appears for the twentieth time he may be insulted and frustrated at the computer's insensitivity to the fact that, by this time, the operator is aware of this bit of medical knowledge. This problem may be solved by designing different modes of program operation so that the experienced user may indicate in his original order that liver disease (or other contra indications) is not present. The computer will then by-pass those bits of information.

The Medication Order Program should be flexible enough to respond to an order in its context. That is, if the user omits information the program should be able to make proper inquiry to obtain a full answer. This, of course, will have been predetermined.

Two points are pertinent on the question of query-response programs. First, users will have to be trained to overcome their exasperation with the machine's need for precision as well as their habit of taking communication short-cuts. Second, the computer memory will have to be routinely updated to reflect current knowledge and practice. This is so not only with drug orders but with all systems where there are variable responses to given factual situations.

A computer system which is to be used on the patient care units in a hospital requires careful human engineering since it must be useful and acceptable to individuals who have little or no technical knowledge in the use of computers but are primarily concerned with patient care. Because of this criterion, the programs will have to be designed to appear to the user in a "conversational mode." In this form, the operator of a terminal would request a specific function by entering a fixed code name for a particular program. Thereafter, the flow of information will be under computer control in that the computer would type a question and the user must respond in a fairly restricted format. The computer may check the answers for validity and may even vary the questions depending on the user's answers. When the computer has received enough information, it will then perform some service (establish a patient record, retrieve and print out information, etc.). This mode of operation is better suited to relatively unsophisticated users than the mode of operation where the user has the option of entering the data in an unspecified format or of changing the program at any step.

All user programs would provide abundant checking of both semantic and syntactic errors. When it is possible for the computer to identify a specific type of error, then an appropriate error message will be returned. An example of this would be the rejection of illegal dates (the entry of a future date would be rejected if the specifications for the program have defined that only the current or a past date is an acceptable entry). Another example would be the refusal of the system to accept an admission to a bed location that is already occupied by another patient. In addition, there must be rapid verification of encoded entries. Thus, it will be common for a nurse to refer to a particular patient by his bed location, e.g., "Mr. Smith in 310." The computer programs would be designed to accept this encoded information, but immediately following entry of such a code will verify the entry by returning the name, age, sex and unit number of this particular patient.

The computer system will contain several features to allow the easy correction of errors. Thus, any number of characters in a message just entered can be erased by using a special key. Another key would give the facility of erasing the whole answer. In addition, the operator may go back to any previous question in order to change an answer, or he may request a clean listing of all the previous dialogue.

In designing the programs, there should be flexibility to account for the fact that operator sophistication may range from a high degree of familiarity with the system to almost no experience. Each of the programs should be able to operate in two modes; in one mode, the questions would be lengthy and detailed; let us call that "long mode". An experienced operator will prefer the "short mode" because there would be less delay in waiting for the computer to type the question. An additional useful feature for the inexperienced user would be one that would allow him to type "HOW" and the computer will type back explanatory information and an example of an acceptable answer.

To establish a communication link between the computer and the user, two operations would be required. The input/output device will normally be in an "OFF" status unless a user would be conversing with the computer. Normally the user will start the conversation. He might do so by pressing a signal key which will cause the computer to return the time and the date and some channel information followed by a starting message, for example, the letters "CALL". The user may then specify the program he desires.

It will also be necessary for the user to inform the computer that he has completed a particular message. When the computer controls the input/output device the user can tell when the message is finished by the fact that the computer has stopped sending characters or by some format convention. The computer, however, has no way of knowing that the user has completed his message unless some action is taken to tell the computer that this is the case.

A key which might be called the "ENTER" key is reserved for this purpose. After the user completes a message, he depresses the "ENTER" key and the computer then begins action upon the message. The "ENTER" key would not cause characters to be printed and thus would not be indicated on the various printouts.

Section 5
Education and Staffing Patterns

Technological implementation is not enough. The success of any system will depend upon the enthusiastic support and active collaboration of individuals from the nursing service, the medical and surgical staffs, the medical record library, the clinical laboratories and hospital administration itself. The introduction of an electronic data processing system can give rise to considerable individual and organizational turmoil. Such agitation can be of serious concern in a hospital care unit and its associated laboratories and professional staff, where effective functioning is completely dependent on the active cooperation of a number of individuals.

Any innovation in the organizational setting will result in modification of the organization. The impact of a new computer system on the various personnel levels within a hospital will no doubt lead to difficulty in adjustment, but it is unlikely that a new system would be completely unacceptable. The real question is, can the process of adjustment be made easier? Knowledge and active participation on the part of hospital personnel will be contingent upon the development of a vigorous and effective educational program. The hospital's approach should be to ascertain attitudes toward the hospital and toward patient care procedures on the part of the individuals who will be concerned with the data-processing operation. It then should attempt to develop educational programs that would guide such attitudes toward the acceptance of the computer and its capabilities.

Perhaps the most controversial aspect of any use of a computer system in patient care activities would be the selection of the persons who will actually operate the remote terminal to enter and retrieve the data. Four possibilities may be suggested: the physician, the nurse, a ward secretary, or a specially trained individual assigned to this function.

It would be convenient for the physician if the terminal could effect a rapid retrieval capability to display the present status of each of his patients. If the physician would have direct access to such a system, he could minimize the amount of time required to assimilate the particular information of interest, and he could use the computer system as a powerful tool to probe various parts of a medical record. In addition, if a physician entered his orders directly, there could be immediate feed-back of information from the drug formulary or laboratory which could be of use both in checking the validity of orders and in supplying current information.

For example, if the physician ordered a certain antibiotic for a particular patient he could be reminded at once of the patient's known allergy to the drug (assuming, of course, a sophisticated format for history and physical examinations which would include such information routinely) and also that another antibiotic had recently been shown to be of greater value. However, there would be disadvantages to having the physician enter his orders directly into the computer system. These include the problem of training him in the use of the terminal and to considerations of economy and space, which would limit the number of terminals that could be located on a single care unit. Few physicians would tolerate having to stand in line while waiting for a terminal to become available to enter orders.

A second possibility would be that the nurse, who would have primary administrative responsibility for patient care procedures, could also assume responsibility for the entry and retrieval of the data involved in such procedures. This would have certain definite advantages, since much of the input data would originate from the nursing staff and much of the output data would be generated for the use of the nursing staff. However, there might be an understandable reluctance on the part of the nursing service to assume such responsibility, since one main goal would be to transfer most record-keeping activities from the nurse so that she might give more time to personal care for the patient.

A third possibility would be that the individual who in some institutions now has a responsibility for many of the clerical duties on a patient care unit (the ward secretary or unit manager) could also be assigned the responsibility for working with the computer system. This would be an attractive possibility, since the ward secretary is usually assigned responsibility for many of the activities which would be carried out through a computer system. It would have the disadvantage that the dialogue would be between the computer and a secretary, so that the immediate feed-back of medical, drug, laboratory and other information would be of less value.

The fourth possibility for terminal operator would be a specially trained individual - a medical record information specialist - whose primary responsibility would be this assignment. If a hospital information system proves to be of significant value in many different functions, a full-time operator may be required. If the computer system would replace a major portion of the present record-keeping activities on a patient care unit, such extra person could be easily justified economically. Another consideration would be that the employment of an information processing specialist might alleviate the current shortage of nurses engaged in nursing services. Yet this possibility has the disadvantages discussed with reference to the ward secretary.

Hospitals vary so widely that it will be necessary to have systems designed to meet the specific needs of the individual institution. But this is a problem to which the computer can effectively and efficiently address itself. Flexibility can be built into standard operating programs so that user programs can be developed to handle the information processing needs of the hospital as those needs continue to grow and the institutions and their personnel become more sophisticated.

The most complex programming imaginable, the best training possible and the most efficient organizational revision conceivable will not overcome present legal barriers to the implementation of a total system at the present time. The next chapter will take up the question of legal impediments to automated medical records.

FOOTNOTES

[4]Spencer, W. A., Vallbonna, C., "Application of Computers in Clinical Practice", J.A.M.A. 191: 917-20, 15 Mar. 65.

[5]For a full description of systems and data processing, see, Enkelis, M, "Systems Concepts and Data Processing Methods: An Introduction.", AAMRL, Chicago, 1968.

[6]Martin, James: PROGRAMMING REAL TIME COMPUTER SYSTEMS, Prentice-Hall, Inc., 1965.

[7]As shall be discussed shortly, questions may be lengthy and detailed or terse and symbolic. The "long mode" will be available for less experienced users. The "short mode" would be used by the experienced user. The programs would be capable of operating in either mode so that even the experienced operator could avail himself of the long mode when that was required.

LEGAL IMPEDIMENTS

Medical records are maintained by hospitals primarily to provide complete information about their patients. These records are, or should be, compilations of information reflecting all data necessary to the care and treatment of patients. The record must contain sufficient information to justify the diagnosis, course and management of the patient's illness.

State licensing laws and the regulatory agencies which enforce them are imposing new and more precise requirements with which the hospital must comply. The "Conditions of Participation" promulgated pursuant to the Medicare law impose requirements which affect the record. In addition, non-governmental bodies, such as the Joint Commission on Accreditation of Hospitals, have promulgated standards which are deemed necessary to insure sound medical care through accurate medical records. Thus, the maintenance of medical records and the accurate and complete formulation of information in those records are regulated by both governmental and non-governmental agencies.

While many records are required to be maintained by hospitals, for example, financial records, vital statistics records and those required under the federal and state pharmacy and drug laws, and while many reports are required to be made, e.g. those relating to communicable diseases and violent wounds, records relating directly to the care and treatment of patients will be our main focus.

The emphasis of this chapter will be on the records of patients. For this purpose, a patient is defined as an individual receiving hospital based or coordinated medical services for which the hospital is responsible. This definition includes those patients who are clearly in-patients, because they are provided room and board and continuous general nursing service in an area of the hospital where patients generally stay overnight. It also includes hospital newborn in-patients as well as other infants. The definition includes home care patients who are hospital patients receiving medical services in their places of residence through an organized hospital home care unit, and for whom records are kept. The definition also includes emergency and out-patients so long as a medical record is maintained for each of their visits to the hospital.

Section 1
Creation and Maintenance of
Medical Records

The regulations and statutes uniformly require the creation and maintenance of medical records. Some regulations contain specific delineations of the contents of medical records, set forth in one place and identified in such a way that it is apparent that the person responsible for drafting the regulation was aware of the importance of medical records requirements. Other regulations contain specific medical record requirements which are scattered throughout the entire body of material. For example, specific medical record references have been found in sections relating to the administrator, medical staff, laboratories, radiology department, dietary department and pharmacy. Some are tucked away in subordinate clauses as if they were matters of minor importance. Other state regulations contain requirements which make only the briefest passing reference to medical records and their contents.

With rare exceptions the requirements have been written without regard to automation. However, regulations in Kansas, Utah, West Virginia and Wisconsin make specific reference to automation. The California regulation has been interpreted to authorize computerization. In Oregon, a statute would appear to permit automation of medical records.

The most precise and complete reference to automation is found in the Utah regulation:

8. MEDICAL RECORD DEPARTMENT
a. GENERAL REQUIREMENTS
*   *   *

(3) Automated Record Systems - Nothing in these rules and regulations shall be construed to forbid the use of properly automated records or computerized orders provided:

(a) It contains proper patient identification.

(b) It contains adequate and sufficient data to establish diagnosis and describe the course and management of the individual patient.

(c) It provides proper physician identification and identification of any other person contributing to any part of the medical record.

(d) Consents for care and procedures and any release from

32

liability from the patient must be signed and witnessed in the usual manner and kept on file.

[Hospital Rules and Regulations, Utah State Division of Health, 1968.]

Other provisions in the Utah regulations specifically require physician's signatures. The language of the quoted section would seem to authorize some method of authentication other than a manual signing of the record. The phrase "proper physician identification" in subsection (c) appears to be broad enough to cover the use of a key or other identification device.

The Kansas regulation contains a general statement with reference to automation:

28-34-9 MEDICAL RECORD DEPARTMENT

* * *

a. Nothing in these regulations shall be construed to prohibit the use of properly automated medical records or use of other automated techniques, provided the regulations stated herein are met.

[Hospital Regulations, 5th Ed. Kansas State Board of Health, 1969.]

The regulations require the signature of the attending physician for each clinical entry as well as the signature of a registered nurse for nursing notes and observations. It seems that the recognition of automation is not strong enough to overcome the specific signature requirement. Thus, the regulation can be interpreted to mean that after the record is made manually it may be placed in machine readable form. This interpretation is supported by the language of the retention section which provides that records must be maintained in a "retrievable form" for twenty-two years after the date of last discharge.

The Wisconsin regulation merely provides "in hospitals using automatic data processing, indexes may be kept on punch cards or reproduced on sheets kept in books." The complete record, then, must still be created and maintained in the usual manual fashion.

The West Virginia regulation permits the preservation of records in original form, microfilm or electronic data process. They also authorize keeping indexes on punch cards.

The California regulation provides:

§280. PATIENTS RECORDS. (a) Records shall be kept on all patients admitted. All required records, either as originals or faithful and accurate reproductions of the contents of such originals, shall be maintained in such a form as to be legible and readily available upon the request of the attending physician, the hospital or its medical staff or any other authorized office, agent or employee of either or of any other person authorized by law to make such a request. [Requirements for Hospital Operation, Cal. Admin. Code, Tit. 17, §280 as amended, eff. Jan., 1969.]

The phrase "faithful and accurate reproductions of the contents of such originals" has been interpreted to permit the application of electronic data processing techniques to maintenance of records.[8]

It would appear that the California regulation, like that of Kansas, would authorize the application of data processing techniques *after* an original record had been manually created.

A statute in Oregon, referring to records generally, provides an authorization for machine processing:

Ore. Rev. Stat. §162.610 (1969)

§162.610 RECORDS REQUIRED BY LAW TO BE IN ENGLISH

(1) With the exception of physicians' prescriptions, all records, reports and proceedings required to be kept by law shall be written in the English language or in a machine language capable of being converted to the English language by a data processing device or a computer.

This statute will provide little support for an automated medical record system.

Many state regulations require that medical records be written. Although this requirement would not seem to pose a major obstacle to automation since the output from an automated system would take the form of a printed, and therefore, *written* record, the implication of some regulations and the clear language of others indicate an intent that "written" means manually created. For example, a Maryland regulation provides:

19010.1 Medical records shall be written or dictated only by the attending physician or interns. They shall be written in permanent ink (not pencil or ballpoint pen)... [Standards and Regulations for Acute, General and Special Hospitals, Department of Health, 1959.]

Several states have similar requirements, to the effect that records should be legibly written by pen.

These provisions, to be sure, were promulgated before automated data processing techniques were in common use. They are nevertheless presently controlling and must be revised somehow to include the expanded methods of recordation. That is, the present regulations will have to be amended, or interpreted to reflect the possibility of electronic collection, recordation, manipulation and reproduction of information from medical records.

The California regulation quoted above, for example originally read in part "All records shall be permanent, either typewritten or legibly written in pen and ink..."

The form of medical records will be discussed in detail later. First let us look at some requirements relating to the contents.

Section 2
Contents of Records

The medical record is composed of at least two distinct parts— although these parts may be made up of several types of itemizations and forms. The first part can be called the information section of the record. It is compiled in the ordinary case upon admission; it details the pertinent particulars of the patient's history such as name, age, reason for admission, date of admission, date of discharge, name, address and telephone number of a responsible person or agency, name of the attending physician, health insurance carrier, if any, and (in some instances) the patient's family history.

The second part of the medical record can be called the clinical section of the record; this is a continuously updated detailed history of the treatment rendered to the patient in the hospital. This part of the record reflects the results of physical examinations, treatments administered, progress reports, physician's orders, clinical laboratory reports, x-ray reports, consultation reports, anesthesia record, operative reports, signed consent forms and nurses' notes.

The medical record is designed to be a complete, up-to-date written record of the history, condition and treatment of the patient and the results of his hospitalization. It is a constant reference. It is the information source for all medical and nursing personnel who treat the patient.

Hospitals are required to maintain records by a variety of statutes and regulations. In most states under the public health laws, those who own, manage or supervise hospitals and other health facilities are required to make records of the personal and statistical particulars relating to their patients or inmates. These requirements, such as those relating to birth, death, autopsy, and the like are promulgated primarily for statistical purposes.

The requirement that hospitals maintain specifically identified medical information, that is, data relating to the kinds of care and treatment rendered to each patient is ordinarily found in hospital regulations. In the usual situation, the legislature delegates power to an administrative agency to control, license and regulate the activities of hospitals. These regulations, among other things, generally set forth *minimum* record requirements. Thus, the delineation of detailed requirements concerning the maintenance and contents of medical records will be found in the promulgations of the administrative agency which has authority over hospitals. However, these promulgations vary.

The states can be divided into three groups: those which set forth in detail the information required; those which specify the broad areas of information required; and those which merely state that medical records shall be adequate, accurate or complete.

Arizona, Iowa and Ohio, for example, have broad descriptive statements which do not specify the items to be included in the medical record. Other states list only a portion of the information which can be included in the medical record.

The Michigan regulations contain a specific itemization of information to be included in the record. They provide:

8: —Records

8:1 —The hospital shall require that accurate and complete medical records be kept on all patients admitted.

8:2 —Patients' records shall include the following:

8:21 —Admission Date.

8:22 —Admitting Diagnosis.

8:23 —History and physical examination.

8:24 —Physician's progress notes.

8:25 —Operation and treatment notes and consultations.

8:26 —The physician's orders.

8:27 —Nurse's notes including temperature, pulse, respiration, conditions observed and medications given.

8:28 —Record of discharge or death.

8:29 —Final diagnosis.

8:3 —Additional records of patients having surgery shall include the following:

8:31 —Details of pre-operative study and diagnosis.

8:32 —The pre-operative medication.

8:33 —The name of the surgeon and his assistants.

8:341 —The method of anesthesia.

8:342 —The amount of anesthetic when measurable.

8:343 —Name of the anesthetist.

8:35 —The post-operative diagnosis, including pathological findings.

8:4 —The report of special examinations such as laboratory, x-ray and pathology shall be kept in the patient's record.

8:5 —Medical records shall be preserved as original records, abstracts, microfilms, or otherwise and shall be such as to afford a basis for a complete audit of professional information. [Rules and Minimum Standards for Hospitals, Michigan Department of Public Health, 1960.]

The Michigan regulation is comprehensive. It is as comprehensive as the medical records principles, standards and interpretations promulgated by the Joint Commission on Accreditation of Hospitals. Since state regulatory agencies tend to set forth minimum requirements, the Joint Commission standards may serve as the guide for hospitals and medical record librarians. As a general rule, subject to many specific exceptions, adherence to the standards promulgated by the Joint Commission on Accreditation of Hospitals would meet state regulations. Moreover, since hospital boards and administrative officers are interested in improving the quality of care received by patients in their hospitals and with acquiring or maintaining their accredited status, the standards promulgated by the Joint Commission receive a respect and adherence equivalent to that received by statutes and regulations.

An additional reason for paying close attention to the standards of the

Joint Commission is the fact that state courts have used them as evidence of the standard of care in negligence cases. Indeed, it is now established in several states that governmental regulations, the hospital's bylaws and rules, community practices as well as the Joint Commission standards may all be used to determine the standard of care by which hospital activity is measured.

It is therefore most important in the development of a system of automated data storage and retrieval of medical record information that the standards promulgated by the Joint Commission with reference to medical records be carefully studied.

The Commission has promulgated a principle of medical record services and five standards to explain and implement the principle.

PRINCIPLE

The hospital shall maintain such facilities and services as are adequate to provide medical records that are accurately documented, readily accessible and can easily be used for retrieving and compiling information.

Standard II relates to the contents of the record. The interpretation is provisional.

Standard II

The medical record shall contain sufficient information to identify the patient clearly, to justify the diagnosis and treatment and to document the results accurately.

Interpretation

The form and detail of the medical record will vary and innovations for its improvement are encouraged. All medical records must contain:

- Identification data and consent forms;

- History of the patient;

- Report of the physical examination;

- Diagnostic and therapeutic orders;

- Observations;

- Reports of actions and findings; and

- Conclusions.

In most instances, the most detailed records pertain to inpatients. Inpatient medical records should include the following:

- Identification data and consent forms. These should include such items as the patient's name, address, age and next of kin, as well as other identifying data and consents as deemed necessary by the hospital's administration and the medical staff.

- History of the patient. This record should incorporate the chief complaint, details of present illness, inventory of systems, past history, social history and family history.

  The history should be a record of the information provided by the patient or by his agent. Opinions of the interviewer should not be recorded in the body of the history. The patient's chief complaint should be stated in a concise manner.

- Report of the physical examination. This report should include all pertinent findings resulting from an assessment of all the systems of the body. If a complete history has been recorded and a physical examination performed within approximately 30 days prior to the patient's admission to the hospital, a legible copy of these reports may be used in the patient's hospital medical record in lieu of the admission history and report of the physical examination, provided these reports were recorded by a member of the medical staff. In such instances, an interval admission note that includes pertinent additions to the history and any subsequent changes in the physical findings must always be recorded.

- Diagnostic and therapeutic orders. These orders shall include any written by authorized house staff members and those individuals who have been assigned practice privileges. Telephone orders shall be accepted and written only by a licensed nurse and this should be limited to urgent circumstances. Such orders should be signed by the responsible practitioner within 24 hours.

- Observations. These reports should include progress notes by the medical staff and house staff, consultation reports, nurses' notes and entries by allied health personnel. Consultation reports should contain a written opinion by the consultant, based on an examination of the patient and his record. The location of the consultant's reports in the record is a matter of local option. Progress notes by the medical staff should give a chronological pertinent report of the patient's course and should be sufficient to describe the changes in each of the patient's conditions and the results of treatment. Nurses' notes and entries by allied health personnel should contain only pertinent, meaningful observations and information. Opinions requiring medical judgment should be written or authenticated only by authorized house staff members and those individuals who have been assigned practice privileges.

• Reports of actions and findings. These reports should include such items as reports of pathology and clinical laboratory examinations, radiology examinations, medical and surgical treatment and any other diagnostic or therapeutic procedures. All diagnostic and therapeutic procedures should be recorded and authenticated in the medical record and may include any reports from out-of-hospital facilities. All treatment procedures performed must be documented in the medical record. The surgeon should record and sign a preoperative diagnosis prior to surgery. Operative notes should be prepared immediately after surgery and should contain a description of the findings, the technique used, the tissue removed or altered and the postoperative diagnosis.

• Conclusions. These should include provisional diagnosis, primary and secondary final diagnosis, clinical resume and necropsy reports. The provisional diagnosis should reflect the responsible practitioner's evaluation of the patient's condition at the time of admission. All relevant discharge diagnoses should be recorded, using the terminology of a recognized system of disease nomenclature. The clinical resume should briefly recapitulate the significant findings and events of the patient's hospitalization, his condition on discharge and the recommendations and arrangements for future care. A copy of the clinical resume always should be sent to the medical practitioner and/or agency responsible for the subsequent care of the patient. A final progress note may satisfy this provision in the case of normal deliveries, normal newborn infants and patients with problems of a minor nature who require less than a 48-hour period of hospitalization. When a necropsy is performed, provisional and anatomic diagnoses

40

should be recorded on the medical record within 72 hours, where feasible and the complete protocol should be made part of the record within three months.

A regular analysis of medical records must be made by a medical staff committee that includes the medical record librarian and representatives from nursing service as well as other persons who substantially contribute to the medical record. This committee should make recommendations relative to any changes in the format of the record as well as to its proper filing, indexing, storage and availability. In addition, the committee should review the medical records to ensure that the recorded clinical information is sufficient for the purposes of medical care evaluation.

It is noteworthy that the new standards anticipate and support change. The interpretation under Standard II states that innovations for the improvement of medical records are "encouraged". Other portions of the standards also indicate an awareness on the part of the drafters of the document that modernization is on its way. For example, the general glossary includes use of a computer key within the definition of "authenticate".

However, these recognitions do not suggest that immediate change is in order. The state laws still provide impediments to the incorporation of a totally automated system within the hospital.

Where the state requirements are more specific and identify information which the Joint Commission standards do not require, the regulations of the state must be obeyed. For example, California's requirements provide that the patient record contain not only nurses' notes but diet orders. Maryland has a provision to the same effect.

The earlier Joint Commission standards did not specifically identify nurses' notes as part of the records. The present interpretations do. Indeed the interpretation under Standard II, quoted above, provides not only for nurses' notes but also for "entries by allied health personnel." There is no definition of that phrase, however, the recognition that persons other than medical or dental practitioners and licensed nurses may write in the record is clear. We've mentioned that the application of medical record automation will create new demands for skills of those who place information in the record. This is emphasized by the language of the standards which provide that nurses' notes and the entries of allied health personnel should contain only pertinent meaningful observations and information. Several state regulations have similar requirements.

Pertinent requirements are also found in statutes not directly related to hospitals. For example, a section of the Kansas Probate Code, reads:

41

Kan. Stat. Ann. §59-2928. RESTRAINT OF PATIENTS.

Restraints shall not be applied to a "patient" unless it is determined by the "head of the hospital" to be required by the "patient's" medical needs. The "head of the hospital" or a member of the medical staff shall sign a statement explaining the medical necessity for the use of any restraints and shall make such statement a part of the clinical record of such "patient".

Provisions in the regulations, and the statutes of several states are to the same effect.

New Jersey imposes an interesting record requirement.

N.J.S.A. §30:4-102. FEMALE PATIENTS TO BE ACCOMPANIED.

No female patient shall be taken to a charitable hospital, relief or training institution unless accompanied by her husband, father, brother, son, family physician or some female of reputable character of mature age. Each chief executive officer shall cause to be made immediately upon receiving a female patient, a record of the names of the persons accompanying her to the institution and their relationship to her.

One wonders if the statute is obeyed or enforced. Nonetheless, it contains a record requirement which would have to form a part of the automated data base in New Jersey.

These are but samples of statutory requirements which relate to the medical record but which are not found in the part of the law dealing specifically with the topic.

As to the contents it can be concluded that any design for an automated medical record system should take into account requirements not only of all of the state statutes and regulations setting forth the required contents of medical records but also those of the Joint Commission on Accreditation of Hospitals.

It is an accepted generalization that much information in the medical record is not worth the effort to place it in a computer. The point is that with or without automation there is a need for an overhaul of medical record systems. Records today are incomplete, inconsistent, illegible, inaccurate and unavailable. Computer capability points the way to new methods of reporting and handling medical record information. The impediments are not only legal but professional.

If change is to be brought about the first step should be in the area of the contents of the record. There should be more uniform definition of what goes into the record and the specific form it should take. There should be more uniformity and standardization of nomenclature. Perhaps we are really saying that the medical schools, the nursing schools, and the schools of the health professions should all agree on nomenclature, on methods of notation, on the responsibility of physicians, residents, interns, nurses and others who legitimately put information in the record.

These goals will be difficult to achieve. There is not yet unanimity on the new standards. Nonetheless, what is needed is a total review of the requirements of all the states and the development of a uniform medical record regulation. Certainly, a uniform system of medical recordation would enhance the quality and the quantity of medical care. More information of higher value would be utilized more rapidly both in the hospital and in other health care facilities.

The pressure for uniformity is felt in all sectors of the health care field. We see it in the area of financing the costs of medical care. We see it in the growing interest in formulary systems tied in with generic name prescribing. We see it in regional medical care programs and comprehensive health planning. Medical records play an important role in all of these areas and many more. With or without automation major revisions are needed in our systems of medical recordation.

Section 3
Form of Records

Record requirements may vary widely not only with respect to the contents but also with respect to the form. Some of the regulations studied specifically require that the medical record be "written". While this requirement would not seem to pose a major obstacle to automation because the output from an automated system could take the form of a printed (and therefore, *written*) record, the implication of some regulations and the clear language of others indicate an intent on the part of the regulatory agency that the record be manually produced.

As noted earlier, the Maryland regulation provides that the record must be written in permanent ink, not pencil or ballpoint pen. The Ohio regulations relating to maternity hospitals contain the following language. "Physicians' orders shall be in the record. They shall be written in ink..." Pennsylvania and South Carolina require that all the records be legibly written by pen or typed. The South Carolina provision goes further to require that orders for medication and treatment are to be written in ink.

The plain meaning of these provisions leaves little room for the inclusion of records electronically prepared and placed on magnetic tape. While, of course, these provisions were promulgated before automated data processing techniques were in common use in relation to hospital information processing, nevertheless, a regulation with that language will have to be interpreted, modified or amended so as to include within its meaning the notion of electronic collection and recordation of medical information.

While this kind of regulatory language imposes no great obstacle, it does require that sufficient effort be expended to modify the regulations. The same cannot be said however, for the requirement that records be signed.

Section 4
Authentication of Records

The requirement that records or a portion of them be signed by the physician or other medical practitioner is one built into a medical records system for the purpose of authenticity. For this reason the mere application of automation to a medical record system cannot be considered to preclude the requirement of authenticity. It has been stated that one of the basic requirements of an information system is system reliability.

Few if any regulations studied did not require a signature or an authentication of some sort for the record. Authentication is the key element in the essential requirements of system reliability and system security.

Significantly, the Joint Commission on Accreditation of Hospitals has recognized the potential applicability of computer technology to medical records by including in the glossary preceding the standards the following definition:

"Authenticated"

To prove authorship, for example, written signature, identifiable initials or computer key. The use of rubber stamp signatures is acceptable under the following strict conditions:

1. The physician whose signature the rubber stamp represents is the only one who has possession of the stamp and is the only one who uses it; and

2. The physician places in the administrative offices of the hospital a signed statement to the effect that he is the only one who has the stamp and is the only one who will use it.

The Joint Commission's interpretations of the standards are both specific and general on the question of authentication. Under Standard I, the interpretation provides as a general proposition: "all entries in the record should be dated and signed." Standard II, quoted in full earlier, contains numerous references to authentication. The interpretation for Standard III provides in part:

> ... The parts of the medical record that are the responsibility of the medical practitioner must be authenticated by him. When members of the house staff are involved in patient care, sufficient evidence should be documented in the medical record to substantiate the active participation of the attending medical practitioner(s) in the supervision of the patient's care. Each clinical event, including the history and physical examination, should be documented as soon as is reasonably possible after its occurrence. All entries to the medical record must be dated. Records of discharged patients should be completed within 15 days.

Taken together the Joint Commission standards indicate a clear intention to maintain the requirement of system reliability. This is so even where the Commission recognizes the potential use of automated data processing.

The Conditions of Participation provide that records are to be authenticated by licensed physicians; the physician must sign the entries he makes; a single signature on the face sheet of the record will not suffice, and the attending physician must countersign at least the history and physical examination and summary written by the house staff.

In the state regulations it is found that Florida requires staff physicians to be responsible for medical history and physical examinations and requires them to sign "for the sake of authentication". In Iowa the provision reads in part, "accurate and complete medical records shall be written for all patients and signed by the attending physician." The Kansas regulations relating to newborns requires the physician to sign reports on the condition of the infant at birth and within 24 hours of discharge, it further requires that all physicians' orders shall be written and dated in ink or indelible pencil and signed by the physician.

In Michigan obstetrical records must contain the physician's signed report of the mother's condition immediately before discharge. Michigan also requires that the newborn record contain the physician's signed report of the physical condition of the infant immediately before discharge. Nebraska requires that the medical record for newborns contain the signed report of the physician on the physical condition of the patient immediately before the discharge. In Ohio the provisions relating to maternity hospitals require that the physician's orders in the record shall be written in ink and signed. The physician may also be required to signify his approval of a patient's discharge by signing the records of the patient and the newborn.

In Pennsylvania the responsible physician must sign all records. It should also be noted that the rules and regulations of the Pennsylvania Department of Public Instruction relating to the hospital intern year require that all directions by the chief of the service, or by the intern at his suggestion, pertaining to diet, medication and management of the case should be written on an order sheet.

Order Sheet
* * *

Each order is the equivalent of a prescription, therefore each should be signed. No attendant can be held responsible for compliance unless the order has been written in ink by a physician in his own hand. The orders should be signed by the chief or intern making them. This order sheet is the original entry, and not a copy of orders taken from a ward book. Any orders delivered by the staff physician given over the phone, must be given to the intern exclusively, and at once transcribed by him on the order sheet and properly designated as a telephone order and duly signed by him....

Progress Sheet
The progress notes are the tell-tale of the professional care of the patient while in the hospital. Frequent notes signed by the physician making them should be recorded in ink.... At the end of the progress notes should be written the physical status of the patient before discharge, the general condition of the patient, the specific condition of the part treated, the instructions for further clinical care or disposal, and the final signature of the staff physician for discharge. [Interpretation of the Laws and the Rules and Regulations for Hospital Intern Year, Bulletin 625 Pa. Dept. of Public Instruction, 1951]

Although these regulations may seem outmoded in light of modern methods of communications, they nevertheless govern the internship programs in teaching hospitals in Pennsylvania. Until they are changed by the Department of Public Instruction, they are requirements which have the force of law.

In South Carolina all notes are required to be legibly written or typed and signed. Orders for medication and treatment are to be written in ink and signed by the physician.

The Washington regulation requires the following items to be written and signed by or under the supervision of the attending physician: medical history, physical examinations and findings, medical orders, private notes, summary, report of patient's costs in the hospital and his condition on discharge, and record of all medical care and treatment.

It is obvious that the signature requirement is a major consideration. But the word "signature" may not necessarily mean the actual handwriting of one's name. In several states the legislative definition of "signature" or "written" is broad enough to include printed signatures. Other states make an exception in the case of written signatures. For example, a Massachusetts statute reads:

Mass. Gen. Laws. Ann. Ch. 4 §7 (1966)

§7. DEFINITIONS OF STATUTORY TERMS; STATUTORY CONSTRUCTION.

"Written" and "in writing" shall include printing, engraving, lithographing and any other mode of representing words and letters; but if the written signature of a person is required by law, it shall always be his own handwriting or, if he is unable to write, his mark.

The statutory language is clear and several cases[9] have construed that language to mean that where a statute (and, of course, a regulation) requires a written signature it means a direct personal act of the person whose name is to be signed.

The Massachusetts statute may be broad enough to include computer-generated writings. Note the language, "and any other mode of representing words and letters". The Michigan statute is similar, except that it does not include the broad language quoted immediately above.

The Pennsylvania statute provides that "written" means every legible representation of letters or numerals upon a material substance, except when used in reference to the signature of an instrument.[10]

The statutes, of course, may be interpreted by the courts to reflect modern techniques of communications. Certain business practices have been recognized to require a change in the meaning of the word signature.

Joseph Denunzio Fruit Co. v. Crane[11] was a complicated contracts case involving, in part, the proper interpretation to be placed on written communications via teletype messages exchanged between certain parties. The court cited with approval several cases which indicated that a "signature" may take a variety of forms including handwritten, printed, stamped, typewritten, engraved, photographed or cut from one instrument and attached to another. It is of interest to note the court's recognition of the teletype machine as a modern device, the use of which satisfied the California statute of frauds.

The court must take a realistic view of modern business practices, and can probably take judicial notice of the extensive
use to which the teletype machine is being used today among
business firms, particularly brokers, in the expeditious transmission of typewritten messages ... this court will hold that
the teletype messages in this case satisfy the statute of frauds
in California.[12]

The New Jersey Supreme Court has adopted a rule which appears to
recognize modern technology. While no interpretations of its language
have been found, the rule, on its face is broad and virtually all-
encompassing.

Rule 1. (13). WRITING

**"Writing" means handwriting, typewriting, printing, photostat-
ing, photography and every other means of recording upon any
tangible thing any form of communications or representation,
including letters, words, pictures, sounds or symbols, or combi-
nations thereof, provided that such recording is (a) reasonably
permanent and (b) readable by sight. When information or
data is recorded by means of a generally accepted method or
system, which is operated with suitable controls to safeguard
the reliability and accuracy of the information or data, and
which is equipped with means for providing a reproduction that
is a "writing", such reproduction shall be treated as the equivalent of the information or data, notwithstanding that the form
of recording does not itself constitute a "writing" as defined by
this rule.**

It would appear that a tape library of medical record information would
be—in the language of the second sentence of the quoted material—(1) recorded by means of a generally accepted method or system, (2) operated
with suitable controls to safeguard the reliability and accuracy of the information and data and (3) equipped with means for providing a reproduction
that is a "writing". We can speculate that in New Jersey if the court rule
were made applicable to all writings an automated medical record information system could be operated without a requirement of a back up manual
system. This speculation is buttressed to some extent by the language of the
hospital regulations of that state which require merely that medical records
be properly written. It must be emphasized that this is speculation. There
has so far been no ruling on the specific question of the applicability of the
rule to the kind of system discussed in this book.

While it is possible to find court cases which interpret the word "signature" or "signed" in such a way as to include methods other than the commonly understood manual writing of a person's name, these decisions are sufficiently distinguishable on their facts as to preclude the making of a general rule that some method other than manual signing is generally acceptable. Thus, the law—taking that to mean the statutes, cases and regulations—precludes the automation of physician's signatures. Consequently, a manual record must be maintained. Automated medical record systems can be adapted—assuming operation feasibility, reasonable costs and techniques for system security and system reliability—but they cannot be operated as the sole medical record system.

At the present time any automated medical record system would have to contemplate the maintenance of a traditional manual system, at least until the questions relating to the "writing" and "signature" requirements are resolved. If change is to be brought about an attempt will have to be made to modify, existing restrictive regulations by approaching the relevant state agencies or the legislative branch. It seems unlikely that the great majority of courts will adopt a position and a rule similar to that of the Supreme Court of New Jersey.

Section 5
Storage and Retention

The hospital medical record is maintained primarily for the use of the hospital and the medical staff in order to provide better patient care. The length of time a record should be retained should be determined on the basis of sound hospital and medical practice. However, the decision as to the period of record retention cannot be made on the basis of administrative and medical determination alone. In many states the regulations provide a specific length of time during which all records must be retained. Several state regulations provide that the record must be kept permanently, while a few require that the records be kept for the period of the statute of limitations for contract or personal injury actions.

The standards of the Joint Commission on Accreditation of Hospitals do not contain a specific stated period of time during which records should be kept. The pertinent Joint Commission interpretation states:

> "... The length of time that records are to be kept is dependent upon the length of time that they may be needed for continuing patient care and for legal, research or educational purposes."

This interpretation also recognizes the need for easy retrieval which an automated system would provide.

The American Hospital Association, however, has recommended that hospitals retain their medical records for 15 years.

The California requirement for record retention is 7 years for records connected with the treatment of a patient. In the case of minors the records shall be kept at least one year after the individual has reached the age of 21, but in no event less than 7 years. California allows original or photographic reproductions to be kept.

The Iowa regulation provides that records shall be kept in accordance with the statute of limitations. Kansas requires that records be retained in retrievable form for 25 years. Nebraska requires that records be preserved for 25 years. New Jersey requires that records be stored for at least 25 years. Pennsylvania provides that records may be destroyed after 15 years if a card file with pertinent information pertaining to the person's hospitalization is maintained. Original records must be kept for three years, then they may be microfilmed. South Carolina requires that the original record be kept for 25 years. Obviously, the retention regulations vary widely from state to state. The state-by-state analysis lists them and what they require.

Where no regulation on the question exists, it has often been suggested that the statute of limitations for contract and tort actions be followed. Retaining the record in any form would not impose a burden on the hospital medical record library and usually that period would be shorter than the time required for medical and research reasons. However, one should be alert to the fact that statutes of limitation generally do not begin to run until a minor has reached the age of adulthood, whatever that may be in the particular state.

On the question of storage of records which have been prepared in machine readable form the costs of the storage medium whether magnetic tape, disk or other form would be a factor of some significance. Of course, once manual records have been indexed, photographed and reduced, many forms are available for storage, access and retrieval.

Where there are regulations on the question these will control. However, in the absence of regulatory requirements, each hospital must determine its own policy with reference to retention. It is clear that each record should be retained for as long as there is a medical and administrative need.

While an automated medical record information system might appear to be the answer to the storage and retention problem, care must be taken to insure in those states requiring that the original record be kept either for a period of time or permanently, the magnetic tape or other storage form used by the system will meet statutory and regulatory requirements. As in the case of signatures, the question of retention as well as that of the form of retention would appear to have to await resolution by judicial interpretation or administrative modification. It seems at first glance, however, that if records can be kept in microfilm, it is but a short step to allow records to be retained in electronic form.

Section 6
Requirements Affecting the Medical Staff

Almost all licensing regulations found impose a general requirement that records be accurate and complete. This requirement imposes a duty on the medical practitioner. In addition, the Conditions of Participation and the standards of the Joint Commission on Accreditation of Hospitals and several licensing regulations specifically require prompt completion of records after the discharge of patients. The Connecticut regulation is illustrative:

Section 19-13-D3 SHORT-TERM HOSPITALS, GENERAL AND SPECIAL

* * *

(5) Medical records shall be completed within fourteen days after discharge of the patient except in unusual circumstances which shall be specified in the medical staff rules and regulations. Persistent failure by a physician to maintain proper records of his patients, promptly prepared and completed, shall constitute grounds for suspending or withdrawing his medical staff privileges. [*Public Health Code of Connecticut*, §19-13-D3 (d) (5), Connecticut State Department of Health, 1964.]

This requirement is made applicable to certain long-term hospitals by other provisions of the regulations. Other states have similar provisions specifically requiring the completion of medical records by practitioners within a reasonable length of time.

Where these regulations exist, it is possible for a staff member to lose his privileges if there is persistent failure to keep records up-to-date. In *Board of Trustees of Memorial Hospital v. Pratt*,[13] the Wyoming Supreme Court held that a hospital governing board had the power to suspend a physician who failed to abide by the medical staff rule requiring records to be kept up-to-date.

Of equal importance is the effect of regulations dealing with completion, or the process by which completion is accomplished. It is one matter for the physician to complete records when they are maintained in manual form, it is quite another when records are found only in machine readable form. Of course, a properly devised system will take the requirement relating to completion by the physician into account. It is to be recognized that the requirement is mandatory in many states.

Section 7
Special Statutory Considerations

Some statutes deal specifically with the confidentiality of research information obtained from hospital records by or on behalf of state departments of health or the state medical association. These studies, reports, interviews, statements, memoranda or other data relating to the condition and treatment of any person for use in the course of studies for the purpose of reducing morbidity or mortality are allowed to be published for the advancement of medical research and medical education. The statutes generally provide that the identity of the person whose condition or treatment is the subject of study is confidential and should not be revealed under any circumstances. The statutes also provide that no liability for damages shall arise or be enforced against any authorized person, institution or organization by reason of providing such information or material, or by reason of having released or published the findings and conclusions of such groups to advance medical research and medical education. The law goes on to say that the information is not admissible as evidence in any legal proceedings.

A statute enacted in Arkansas in 1969 relates to information, data and reports received by the Arkansas Regional Cancer Registry. It provides that such information shall be used only for statistical, scientific and medical research purposes. The information is to go to the computerized state cancer registry. Physicians, surgeons, dentists, institutions or hospitals furnishing such information with respect to malignant diseases are deemed not to have violated any confidential relationship and they will not be held liable in damages to any person for betrayal of a professional secret.

Several states have statutes which specifically relate to the records or reports in mental hospitals or in the department of mental health. They all provide for confidentiality of the information in those records.

Nebraska, Pennsylvania, Arkansas and other states specifically grant medical staff or hospital utilization committees immunity from liability for inspecting the records of patients in the performance of their duties of evaluation and of patient care.

While these laws may not appear to be directly relevant to questions of legal impediments since they purport to provide protection against liability for handling of information about patients, it is necessary to view them in the light of a total automated system when they may become part of the data base. Retrieval for purposes of disclosure will have to include the capability to prevent the output of this research, utilization and mental health

52

information. This information may or may not be put into the system at all, but it should not, in any event, be part of the patient's record.

As we can see the rules and regulations of the various states impose many requirements upon medical records. Some of these pose severe restrictions on the creation of a totally automated medical record system. Yet none of these are absolutely insurmountable. Any institution or group of institutions contemplating the development of a system for automated medical record keeping will have to start with a review of the regulations, cases and statutes of the state which affect the operation of medical records. Moreover, any new system will have to provide for system reliability and system security. We shall have more to say on this in the next chapter, dealing with confidentiality.

FOOTNOTES

[8] Letter dated July 24, 1969 from Howard A. Worley, Chief Bureau of Health Facilities Licensing and Certification signed by Ralph A. Bruns, Regional Chief, California Department of Public Health.

[9] See, e.g., Irving v. Goodimate Co., 320 Mass. 454, 70 N.E.2d 414 (1946); Finnegan v. Lucy, 157 Mass. 439, 32 N.E. 656 (1892).

[10] Pa. Stat. Ann. tit. 46, §601(110) (1969).

[11] 188 F.2d 569 (9th Cir. 1951), *cert. denied,* 342 U.S. 820 (1951), *aff'g.* 79 F. Supp. 117 (S.D. Cal. 1948).

[12] *Id.,* 79 F. Supp. at 128.

[13] 72 Wyo. 120, 262 P.2d 682 (1953).

CONFIDENTIALITY

In the view of many the most significant problem related to the development of automated medical record systems is the problem of privacy. Indeed, protection of the confidentiality of information is a major continuing concern. However, as we have discussed there are two demands upon any information system which have primary importance. They are system security and system reliability.

Security and reliability are independent and equally forceful imperatives for any information system. The most secure and protected system is worthless if there are inadequate protections against unauthorized disclosure, whether intentional or unintentional. This is so with any information system, it is particularly so with reference to a medical record information system.

The law seeks to provide an assurance of reliability by requiring the written signatures of physicians, nurses and other health professionals on portions of the record. This requirement fixes responsibility on the persons whose actions we wish to judge or monitor. Many administrative regulations and some statutes contain explicit signature requirements.

However, the law is not so precisely defined on the question of protecting confidentiality. A few statutes or regulations specifically require that records remain confidential. But, confidential to whom and for what purpose? There are some who feel that the record is so confidential that the patient should never see it. As we shall see the patient has a legally enforceable interest in the information in the record. There are others who feel that confidentiality is an aging concept. Today the need is for information flow not information restriction. The State licensing regulations reflect both the need to protect the information in the medical record and the need to disclose it.

Standard III of the Joint Commission on Accreditation provides that medical records shall be confidential, current and accurate. The interpretation contains language which further elaborates this notion. It recognizes that in the treatment of mental disorders, certain portions of the record are "so confidential" that extraordinary means may be taken to preserve their privacy.

A contrary view supports automation of medical records precisely because routine scanning of records might reveal mental aberrations in individuals which cause them at unexpected times to commit mass murder. We could, so the theory goes, prevent such loss of life if we had an early warning system, so to speak, which would be feasible with a regional or national automated medical record system. If medical science could develop more precise definitions of warning signals and if we could create monitoring systems which would at once protect privacy and allow detection and apprehension of deviant personalities, society would be safer. The dangers of this kind of system are clear and present.

The case law, of course, contains instances of civil actions brought for violation of a right to privacy. These cases have been relied upon to expand the application of the doctrine of the right of privacy to hospitals. Persons in the health professions also have a keen sense of the importance of confidentiality and in accordance with this notion, ethical requirements have been stated in professional standards with some degree of specificity. The point is, however, that there are few legal guidelines to which one can refer in developing a set of protections of confidentiality in an automated medical record system.

Obviously physicians, nurses and other hospital personnel are aware of their ethical and legal responsibilities. They will continue to maintain high standards of care with respect to automated records. However, the same requirements apply to persons who operate the machine system, that is, persons who are not health professionals or technicians. They, too, are aiding in the provision of health services and should be deemed to fall within the broad description of persons who have a legitimate reason to deal with the patient's medical information. They have a concomitant responsibility to protect the confidentiality of that information.

In fact, data processing personnel stand in approximately the same relationship to the patient and his information as do the personnel in the medical records department. It is apparent that the ethical standards to which medical record librarians are subject should apply to data processing personnel.

While the rules, notions and assumptions of confidentiality of medical record information will not act as an absolute prohibition to the development of an automated system, they will impose a continuing responsibility of care in the disclosure of information to anyone outside the ambit of legitimate interest. Consequently, all hospital personnel should be required to observe the rule of non-disclosure except for the legitimate needs of the patient, hospital, physician and, at times, the public.

If problems exist with the implementation of an automated system controlled exclusively by the hospital, many more are present where the hospital joins in a time-sharing system or where the hospital utilizes a service bureau.

While the law of privacy as it presently exists can provide some degree of compensation for the violation of the right of privacy, the principal responsibility for developing routines, systems and procedures to provide protections against disclosure rests with the professions and the automation industry. Thus, responsibility for the development and enforcement of internal standards rests with hospitals and health care institutions and the responsibility for the development of machine and programming capabilities rests with the manufacturers and systems experts. The role of the law - or more precisely, the lawmakers - will most likely be passive. Yet, lawmakers will act when experts present persuasive information and show the course to follow.

But there will have to be a clear-cut direction. Presently, we are ambivalent in the sense that society feels the need both to disclose the information and to keep it safe from disclosures.

Section 1
The Confidential Nature of Medical Record Information

There is a conflict in our public policy with respect to the confidentiality of medical information. The conflict arises because the medical record is a peculiar type of property. In purely physical terms it belongs to the hospital and it should be used to aid in the provision of medical care and in the continuing educational process that is inherent in the delivery of health services. Nevertheless, the record contains such detailed information about the personal particulars of the patient that there is general recognition of a need for confidentiality.

On the one hand there is a felt need to disclose medical record information to those who can or must utilize it to participate in the delivery of medical care services, and on the other hand there is an equally strongly felt need to keep the information secret. This conflict between disclosure and nondisclosure is manifested in the decisions of many courts and in the language of many statutes on the point.

An example of the conflict is the so-called physician-patient privilege. That privilege is a statutorily created prohibition which prevents the physician who attends the patient from testifying about the diagnosis, care and treatment he rendered unless the patient consents in some manner. The privilege protects communications between the patient and the practitioner; these communications are called confidential. The privilege must be exercised by the patient; that is, the privilege belongs to the patient. It does not belong to the physician. The privilege generally applies to hospital records and it has been applied to nurses.

The vast majority of litigated cases today involve questions of law or fact where medical information is relevant evidence. These include actions to recover damages for personal injury or wrongful death; to collect proceeds under life, accident or health insurance contracts; for malpractice; and involving testamentary documents such as wills and trusts. Proceedings in divorce, workmen's compensation and lunacy, as well as criminal prosecutions involving injuries, abortions, sexual offenses and homicide are also a large class of cases. In most, if not all, of these cases, the testimony of a physician, nurse or other health professional and the information in a hospital record is necessary to aid the court in finding the facts. Yet the privilege - or rather the notion of confidential communications - may prevent the testimony of precisely those persons or records which would be most helpful in ascertaining the facts.

Moreover, the notion of the confidentiality of health communications may create a state policy towards disclosure of information in non-testimonial settings. Thus, even in states with no statute providing a testimonial privilege there may be a right of action for disclosure of information gained in a confidential setting.

For example, in *Hague v. Williams*[14] plaintiffs were parents who sued their physician for disclosures he made to an insurer of an infant who had died as a consequence of a congenital heart defect. The parents were not informed by the doctor of this ailment and, of course, had not consented to the disclosure. The lower court dismissed the suit. The Supreme Court of New Jersey in upholding the judgment of the lower court, spelled out the competing concerns. At the time, there was no statutory testimonial privilege in New Jersey. The court took note of this and said it was the state policy to receive information in testimonial situations because the benefits derived from the correct disposal of litigation outweighed the possible harm to the physician-patient relationship. Then the court said:

> However, the same philosophy does not apply with equal rigor to non-testimonial disclosure. The above ethical concepts, although propounded by the medical profession under its own code, are as well expressive of the inherent legal obligation which a physician owes to his patient. The benefits which inure to the relationship of physician-patient from the denial to a physician of any right to promiscuously disclose such information are self-evident. On the other hand, it is impossible to conceive of any countervailing benefits which would arise by according a physician the right to gossip about a patient's health.

The court held, in this case, that the disclosure was justifiable because the physical condition of the patient was an element of the claim. It concluded, however, by saying:

> ... ordinarily a physician receives information relating to a patient's health in a confidential capacity and should not dis-

close such information without the patient's consent, except where the public interest or the private interest of the patient so demands. Without delineating the precise contours of the exceptions, it may generally be said that the disclosure may, under such compelling circumstances, be made to a person with a legitimate interest in the patient's health.

The New Jersey court spelled out the broad outline of a policy which may be helpful in determining the limits of disclosure in the context of an automated medical record system. No question should arise if physicians associated with the patient's case obtain information about that case. The same would hold for nurses and allied health personnel in the hospital.

Thus, the rules, notions and assumptions of confidentiality of medical record information do not act as a prohibition to the implementation of an automated system. They do, however, impose a continuing responsibility of care in the disclosure of information to anyone outside the ambit of legitimate interest. Consequently, all hospital personnel—from the governing board to the maintenance department—are required to observe the rule of nondisclosure except for the legitimate needs of the patient, hospital, physician and the public.

On the question of privacy it can be concluded that the implementation of an automated system will provide some protections against unauthorized disclosure but it also presents new problems. As is usually the case, the primary responsibility for an orderly and sensible transition from the information systems we now use to one which will more and more utilize the new machines and techniques is upon the health professionals and engineers who create and implement those systems.

Section 2
The Patient's Right to the Information

The hospital's relationship with the patient is similar to that of the physician. As a custodian of medical information the hospital must always be aware of the confidential nature of the relationship of the information received. Moreover, the hospital must be aware of the privilege inherent in the patient to see the information. This is not to suggest that the patient has a right to see his record at any and all times. The patient has a right to see the information in his records but he must have a legitimate reason. The same requirement would apply to those who stand in the patient's shoes as a result of an authorization received from the patient.

A few statutes have given the patient, his physician or authorized agent the right to examine and copy the record. In Connecticut each hospital receiving state aid must permit a patient or his physician or authorized attorney to examine the hospital record, including the history, bedside notes, charts, pictures and plates and they must permit copies of these to be made. In Massachusetts and Wisconsin medical records of licensed hospitals may be inspected by a patient, or his attorney pursuant to written authorization of the patient and copies must be furnished upon payment of a reasonable fee. New Jersey permits hospitals to allow examinations of patients' records not only to persons who have an authorization from the patient but also to persons against whom a claim is asserted for compensation or damages for personal injuries. Hospital lien laws may allow inspection by persons against whom a claim is asserted. Several state statutes specifically allow the disclosure of information, reports and other data procured in the course of medical study for the purpose of reducing morbidity or mortality by health departments, state medical societies, allied medical societies, or in-hospital staff committees of accredited hospitals. They also provide that furnishing such information shall not subject any person, hospital, sanitarium, nursing or rest home or any agency to any action for damages or other relief.

Where there is no clear statutory authority spelling out a patient's right, generally, to examine his record, the decision to allow or not to allow the patient or his authorized agent to see the record can be made up on the basis of an administrative judgment, taking into account the circumstances of the particular case. Ordinarily no adverse legal consequences will arise if the hospital refuses to allow a patient to see his record, where there is not a refusal to comply with a court order. It should be remembered that the patient can obtain relief from the courts and if the court orders disclosure to the patient, the order must be obeyed. The possibility of a suit for damages based on a refusal by a hospital to allow the patient to see his record seems remote.

That medical information might be contained on magnetic tape does not, in this context, pose additional problems to the hospital. In fact, rapid retrieval and disclosure may be enhanced because the record is in machine processable form. However, there will undoubtedly be increased costs to the patient or his authorized representative because of the cost of data processing equipment and machine time. This, however, presents no legal problem so long as the charge to the patient is not unreasonable.

Section 3
Medical Records as "Public Records"

A few courts have indicated that hospital records are in the nature of public records and therefore should be available to persons who can show a legitimate interest in the information. Medical and hospital records which are required to be kept by state statute or regulation can be considered public in the sense that they are maintained in obedience to a command of a governmental authority. Moreover, records maintained by or in governmental offices or institutions are also public records in the sense that they are maintained by those agencies. However, the fact that a record is made and maintained by a public institution or by a private institution pursuant to a legislative or administrative command does not create a right, generally recognized as applicable to the public at large to see and examine records.

There are no clear cut rules by which one can determine whether or not records are public. Often a statute will declare certain records to be public, that is, open and available to the general population, but in the absence of a specific statute, the determination as to the nature of a particular record may be left to the custodian of the record. It is clear that the record maintained by a non-governmental hospital is not a public record in a broad and general sense. The fact that records are required to be maintained does not in and of itself make the record public or create a right in the public to view it. Indeed, even where courts have declared that a particular person or class of persons may see a record, there has to be a showing of legitimate interest.

The patient may be able to gain access to information in the records but this is not because of statutory or regulatory requirements relating to maintenance or retention. In the final analysis, where there is no specific statute or regulation the question of disclosure of information to the patient or his agent or to the general public is an administrative one.

With reference specifically to automated medical record information systems, the mere fact that records are maintained in an automated library or the fact that a statute or regulation may allow the maintenance of records in such form should not give rise to a decision or ruling that these records are public in a general sense.

Even the creation of a regional or national medical data center would not seem to create a right in the general public to view information. The objection to regional or national medical data centers, however, is not so much the possibility that the general public will gain access. The fear has been expressed that a file of that nature may be misused by those who have authority to create, maintain and search it. The notion that even some persons - governmental officials or others - will have access, to medical information, has moved many to oppose automation of medical records in any form. Obviously, new safeguards and protective measures will have to be erected.

Section 4
Permissible Disclosures

The persons and agencies who may be found to have legitimate interests in the information contained in a hospital record have multiplied tremendously in recent years. Not too long ago the only persons who had such an interest were the hospital, the patient and perhaps the physician. Today, however, with many millions covered by medical and hospital insurance contracts of one form or another, with the growth of organized medical research and with the expansion of governmental participation in the medical care field, third parties have come to possess a recognizable interest in the records of most patients.

The question to be considered is what revisions in the traditional policies regulating the release of information are required in the light of changes in the circumstances of medical and hospital care.

As has been pointed out, the data in the medical record are of two types: informational and clinical. The data can also be classified broadly in terms of confidentiality and non-confidentiality. Confidential data is that which is obtained professionally and is found generally in the clinical part of the record. Non-confidential data relates to the identification of the patient and the dates of his admission, and is found in the informational part of the record. Non-confidential data may be released at the discretion of the hospital authorities without written consent of the patient. However, even this type of information should be released with care. Thus, in the usual case, the patient's name and the dates of admission and discharge, and the name of his physician may be given upon request, without untoward consequences. However, disclosure that an unmarried woman was admitted to a maternity hospital or that a person was admitted to a mental hospital for observation might be improper. Therefore, a conservative policy in releasing such information is indicated.

The principal consideration bearing upon disclosure should be the nature of the information requested and the persons or agencies requesting the information. In the routine case, no problems will arise with respect to legal liability or poor patient relations if the facts in the record are divulged to those with a legitimate interest.

Subpoenas

The presentation of a medical record for use as evidence in a court or other duly constituted tribunal is proper. When the hospital receives a court order, it has no recourse but to obey that order. However, the custodian of the medical records is not obligated to present the records except upon proper court order or subpoena. These are generally of two types.

The subpoena is a form of legal process which is designed to cause a witness to appear and give testimony. It commands the witness to appear before a specified court or officer thereof at a specified time. There may be a penalty for failure to appear.

The other type is called the subpoena duces tecum, which is a subpoena requiring not only that the witness attend but also that he bring to the court certain books, documents, papers or records described in the subpoena. In some states there is a third type of subpoena which is used as a pre-trial discovery procedure to expedite the trial of cases. It is sometimes called a notary subpoena.

It is to be noted that even though records are subpoenaed it does not necessarily follow that they will be admitted or received into evidence by the court. The admission or exclusion of evidence at the time of trial is governed by rules of evidence. Thus, the records may or may not be admissible according to the facts, questions of law and circumstances of the particular case. In any event, when a medical record is summoned to the court by a subpoena duces tecum, the librarian or other custodian of the record should follow certain procedures.

(1) The requested record should be printed out and read so as to insure that it is complete, but only those records specifically requested should be brought to court.

(2) The print out should be kept in a special place to prevent removal, tampering or misplacement before the appointed date.

(3) A memorandum should be made indicating the portions of the record which have been printed out and taken to court, as well as the date, time, and names of the litigants.

(4) Possession of the record should not be given to anyone unless the librarian or other custodian is instructed to do so by the court or other official, and in that case a receipt should be obtained.

(5) No one should be allowed to examine the record prior to an instruction from the court or other official. The party issuing the subpoena has no right to see the record until examination ordered by the court.

(6) The conduct of the librarian on the stand should be grave and dignified. Answers should be concise and direct, and only in response to the question. No information should be

volunteered. Answers should be made only as to matters known; in the usual case this will relate to the identification of the record.

(7) Before the appointed date for answering the subpoena, the librarian might consult with hospital counsel as to the specific local practices regarding subpoenas.

Hospitals should formulate policies and procedures regarding the release of information to persons not employed by or working with the hospital, which will recognize not only responsibilities to the patients but also the legitimate interests of insurance companies, attorneys, medical research and education, governmental agencies and the press. Release of information should always be under the control of an employee who is trained in techniques for processing requests to the computer data base. A set of procedures will have to be developed whereby only authorized persons will have access to the data base and only authorized requests will be processed. These procedures will have to include techniques which promote rapid and efficient authorization. Moreover, the retrieval programs will have to be capable of permitting sophisticated selections of the information in the data base.

Insurance Companies

Many requests to review records come from third-party sources of payment. Insurance companies of various kinds fall into this category. In the past there has been an administrative reluctance to allow insurance representatives to examine and review patients' records; however, a change in point of view has taken place. This change in attitude is good and will not work to the detriment of the hospital. Certainly, the patient who has paid premiums for medical and hospital insurance recognizes and anticipates that certain administrative steps are necessary to assure payment of his bill. But he also desires that there be no undue red tape involved. It may be feasible therefore to adapt standard and approved claims forms and authorization forms already used in the field for computer use. If additional information is required by the insurance carrier, then the hospital may be justified in making a reasonable charge for handling. In any case, the hospital should work out an agreement with local representatives of insurance carriers so that delay and controversy can be avoided.

Attorneys

Where attorneys request to examine or review the record, written authorization of the patient whose record is to be examined should be required. Some hospitals also require the authorization of the attending physician. No blanket administrative rule can be laid down in this situation, but generally the physician has no legal right to prevent the patient's attorney from examining the record. The physician's authorization may be obtained as a matter of courtesy. Whether or not the entire record should be disclosed will depend on the facts and circumstances of the case. In this area the hospital should call upon hospital counsel to aid it in determining the disposition to be made of the attorney's request. It must be remembered that the attorney has the ultimate weapon: a subpoena.

Thus, where an attorney seeks to review a record without the patient's authorization, his request should be politely refused and he should be told to obtain the patient's authorization. Where the patient has authorized an attorney to review the record the hospital may make a charge for the costs of retrieving the information from the data base.

A question may arise relating to the amount of information to be given to the attorney. Several states provide by statute that a patient or his authorized representative has a right to review his record. There is also growing judicial authority on the point. The question of the amount of information to be disclosed assumes even greater significance in the context of automated medical record systems because presumably there will be more information stored in the data base than is presently contained in the medical record. Theoretically, at least, the patient's right to the information in the record includes whatever the record contains in whatever form. In the future, statutes or decisions may define the scope of inquiry more precisely.

In *Bishop Clarkson Memorial Hospital v. Reserve Life Insurance Company*,[15] the basic question was whether a hospital could deny access to a person who had an authorization from the patient and a legitimate interest in the record. The hospital was willing to permit the insurer to inspect and copy the record, under supervision of a physician. It was also willing to furnish abstracts of the record. The company objected, asserting a right to inspect original records unaccompanied by a physician. The court held that the hospital could not deny access to the original records. However, the court did place a qualified restriction upon access. It said that the right to inspect the records would be limited "where the bona fide and good faith judgment of the patient's doctor dictates and he certifies under oath that the records not be released to the patient or his authorized representative in the best interests of the patient's health." This qualification would seem to have limited application for in the vast majority of cases disclosure would not be detrimental to the patient's health.

A Michigan statute relating to medical research information provides that this information, when voluntarily shared with the state health commissioner in connection with medical research studies conducted by him or jointly with other persons, agencies or organizations, is confidential and to be used solely for the purposes of medical research. It is further provided that the furnishing of medical research information pursuant to the statute shall not subject any physician, hospital, sanatorium, and like persons or organizations to any action for damages or other relief. However, any disclosure not made pursuant to the law is declared to be a crime. There are similar research statutes in several states.

Governmental Agencies

If the hospital is provided with positive identification of the person requesting information for the police or other law enforcement body, the hospital should provide all reasonable assistance in releasing non-confidential data. As to clinical data, which may be confidential in nature, each case must be determined on its own facts. However, it should be remembered that law officers have a final recourse through the use of a subpoena or other legal process, and the hospital will not suffer in requiring its use.

With reference to other governmental agencies, such as those handling workmen's compensation cases, the Veteran's Administration or the coroner's office, the same considerations apply. Certain of these agencies are granted express authority to obtain information from medical records, and in the alternative they will have the right to subpoena the records. It is to be noted that several states have hospital lien laws which allow the disclosure of information to the parties in the case without the authorization of the patient. The medical records librarian should always be given a copy of the notice of lien so that he or she will be ready to handle requests that may come for the release of information for which the patient will have given no authorization.

Again, the automated system should allow selective retrieval of information so that only that portion of the record which is relevant to the inquirer's specific needs will be printed out from the data base.

News Media

In several states policies have been promulgated by hospital associations outlining the relationship that should exist between hospitals and representatives of the press, radio and television. Every hospital, individually or through its state or regional association, should promulgate codes of conduct, which will recognize the legitimate interests of the patient and the press, radio and television. Distinctions should be made between police and accident cases on the one hand where the newsworthiness of the event supports some disclosure without consent, and private cases where no information should be released without consent. In any event the distinction between confidentiality and non-confidentiality of information must be maintained. Thus, in an accident case it is permissible to describe the condition of the patient in general terms.

Information for the news media should be carefully prepared by the medical record librarian in cooperation with the patient's physician and the hospital's public relations officer or other person who handles those matters. (In some cases it may be the administrator.) The introduction of an automated medical record system will not change the necessity for carefully devised procedures for controlled release of information to the press.

Section 5
Statutory Reporting Requirements

Hospitals are required to make reports to a variety of health and welfare agencies on a variety of subjects. In no case should the adoption of an automated system inhibit the hospital's ability to meet these requirements. Indeed, the legal obligation may be more easily met by such systems precisely because the reports can be generated directly from the data base through the application of specially designed programs.

The question of confidentiality of medical record information is not clear-cut. There are competing interests which will arise continually. The introduction of an automated medical record system will, among other things, enhance the ability to disseminate information. It will be necessary under any system to maintain rules and procedures which protect against unauthorized disclosure. These procedures will have to govern the personnel who handle information flow to the individuals and agencies discussed above. The procedures will also have to contain safeguards and protective measures which apply to the methods of processing the medical record data.

FOOTNOTES

[14]37 N.J. 328, 181 A.2d 345 (1962).

[15]350 F.2d 1006 (8th Cir. 1965).

SAFEGUARDS AND PROTECTIVE MEASURES

In this chapter various methods of providing information privacy for remotely accessible on-line, shared-resource information systems, will be explored. Such systems, especially the remote terminals and the communication network are vulnerable to threats to privacy ranging from accidental dumping of information as a result of machine or program failures, to deliberate penetration using sophisticated equipment. Deliberate attacks are to be expected since the returns (or more precisely, the payoffs) can be high.

To put this in proper perspective, the following case will be illustrative:

In *McDaniel v. Atlanta Coca-Cola Bottling Company,*[16] the plaintiff brought an action for invasion of privacy against the bottling company for secretly installing a receiving set in plaintiff's hospital room by means of which an agent of the company could listen to her conversations with her husband, her physician, and the nurses who attended her. The company claimed that it installed the set and listened to plaintiff's conversations because it believed that her claim of harm caused by glass from an exploding soda bottle was fraudulent. The jury returned a verdict for the defendant and the Georgia Court of Appeals affirmed the judgement, holding that the jury could properly receive evidence which would mitigate the claim or the damages. The court nevertheless recognized that the plaintiff's right to privacy had been invaded. The court also said that the invasion occurred even though the use of the information was restricted to the company and was not published or commercialized. The original intrusion was the prohibited wrong.

In the interval between 1939, when the *McDaniel* case was decided, and the present many sophisticated techniques and devices have been developed. Indeed, electronic invasions of privacy are so threatening that Congress has held extensive hearings on the matter.

This discussion is based on the following model of an information system:

(a) A central processing facility of one or more processors (computers) and an associated memory hierarchy;

(b) A set of programs usually called systems software which provides the actual capabilities of the information system;

69

(c) A set of information files—some private, others shared by a number of users;

(d) A set of public or private query terminals at geographically remote locations; and

(e) A communication network of common carrier, leased, or private lines.

See Chart, Page 71.

This shared, on-line system will be referred to throughout as "the system." Resources of the system will be available at any one time by multiple users and will be viewed as a time-shared system.

Data privacy can be jeopardized in many ways. The most likely are:

1. The inadvertent disclosure of information to unauthorized individuals through system failure.

2. "Wire-tapping" of the data transmission network by unauthorized individuals.

3. The uncontrolled access to information by persons such as insurance investigators, government agency personnel, employers and credit bureau personnel.

The first case would be caused by errors in design or operation of the functional components of the system. The second would result from insufficient protection in the communications facilities. And the last case would occur as a result of failure in the management and supervisory control of the system.

Relative to these potential intrusions some protective countermeasures shall be discussed including:

1. Development of organizational safeguards within the system facilities.

2. Establishment of legal parameters for the operation of the system.

3. Shielding to reduce electro-magnetic emanations.

4. Use of one-time passwords for access control.

5. Application of privacy transformations to conceal information in user-processor communications and in data files.

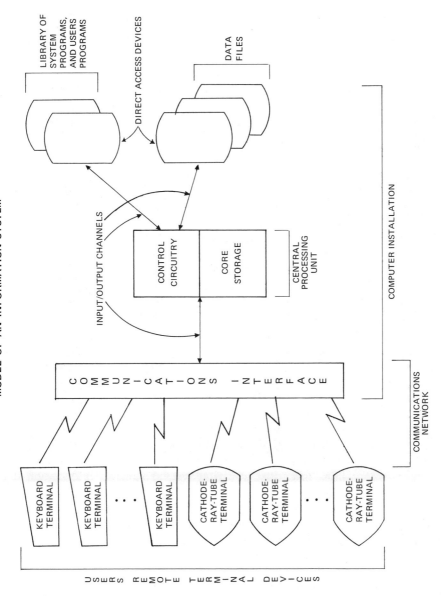

MODEL OF AN INFORMATION SYSTEM

6. Monitoring of all accesses and recording of attempted penetrations.

7. Systematic verification of hardware and software integrity.

It appears possible to engineer various privacy protection techniques into information systems so that the cost of protection is proportional to the amount of information received, and is borne largely by those users who desire privacy for their communications and/or files.

Section 1
Threats to Information Privacy

Privacy of information in the system is lost either by accidentally or deliberately induced disclosure. The most common causes of accidental disclosures are failures of the computer, sometimes called hardware, and use of partially debugged programs. Improvements in hardware reliability and various memory protection schemes are generally suggested as countermeasures. Deliberate efforts to infiltrate an on-line, time-shared system can be classified as either passive or active.

Passive infiltration may be accomplished by wiretapping or by electromagnetic pickup of information at any point in the system. Although considerable effort has been applied to counter such threats to defense communications, nongovernmental approaches to information privacy usually assume that communication lines are secure, when in fact they are the most vulnerable part of the system. Techniques for penetrating communication networks may be borrowed from the well-developed art of listening in on voice conversations. (While the minimum investment in equipment is higher than that required to obtain a pair of headsets and a transducer, it is still very low since a one-hundred-dollar tape recorder and code conversion table suffice.) Clearly, digital transmission of information does not provide any more privacy than, for example, the Morse Code. Nevertheless, some users seem willing to entrust to digital systems valuable information that they would not communicate over a telephone.

Active infiltration—an attempt to enter the system directly to obtain or alter information in the files—can be overtly accomplished through normal access procedures by:

• Using legitimate access to a part of the system to ask unauthorized questions (e.g., requesting payroll information or trying to associate an individual with certain data), or to "browse" in unauthorized files.

72

- "Masquerading" as a legitimate user after having obtained proper identifications through wiretapping or other means.

- Having access to the system by virtue of a position with the information center or the communication network but without a "need to know" (e.g., system programmer, operator, maintenance, and management personnel).

An active infiltrator may attempt to enter the system covertly (i.e., avoiding the control and protection programs) by:

- Using entry points planted in the system by unscrupulous programmers or maintenance engineers, or probing for and discovering "trap doors" which may exist by virtue of the combinatorial aspects of the many system control variables.

- Employing special terminals tapped into communication channels to effect:

  - "piggy back" entry into the system by selective interception of communications between a user and the processor, and then releasing these with modifications or substituting entirely new messages while returning an "error" message;

  - "between lines" entry to the system when a legitimate user is inactive but still holds the communication channel;

  - cancellation of the user's sign-off signals, so as to continue operating in his name.

In all of these variations the legitimate user provides procedures for the infiltrator to obtain proper access. The infiltrator is limited, however, to the legitimate user's authorized files.

More than an inexpensive tape recorder is required for active infiltration, since an appropriate terminal and entry into the communication link are essential. In fact, considerable equipment and know-how are required to launch sophisticated infiltration attempts.

With regard to the objectives of infiltration attempts against information systems from the point of view of potential payoff, it is enough to indicate the types of activities that an infiltrator may wish to undertake:

- Gaining access to desired information in the files, or discovering the information interests of a particular user.

- Changing information in the files (including destruction of entire files).

- Obtaining free computer time or the unauthorized use of proprietory programs.

Depending on the nature of the filed information, a penetration attempt may cause no more damage than satisfying the curiosity of a potentially larcenous programmer. Or it may cause great damage and result in great payoffs; e.g., illicit "change your dossier for a fee," or industrial espionage activities. (See Table I for a summary of threats to information privacy.)

More sophisticated infiltration scenarios can be conceived as the stakes of penetration increase. The threat to information privacy should not be taken lightly or brushed aside by underestimating the resources and ingenuity of would-be infiltrators.

Table I

SUMMARY OF THREATS TO INFORMATION PRIVACY

Nature of Infiltration	Means	Effects
Accidental	Computer malfunctioning; user errors; undebugged programs	Privileged information dumped at wrong terminals, printouts, etc.
Deliberate Passive	Wiretapping, electro-magnetic pickup examining carbon papers, etc.	User's interest in information revealed; content of communications revealed
Deliberate Active	Entering files by: "Browsing"; "Masquerading"; "Between lines"; "Piggy-back" penetration	Specific information revealed or modified as a result of infiltrator's actions

Section 2
Countermeasures

The spectrum of threats discussed above can be countered by a number of techniques and procedures. Some of these were originally introduced into time-shared, multi-user systems to prevent users from inadvertently disturbing each other's programs. Others found their beginning in requirements to protect privacy in communication networks.

Access Control

Access management techniques are aimed at preventing unauthorized users from obtaining services from the system or gaining access to its files. The procedures involved are authorization, identification, and authentication. Authorization is given for certain users to enter the system, gain access to certain files, and request certain types of information. For example, a researcher may be permitted to compile earnings statistics from payroll files but not to associate names with salaries. Any user attempting to enter the system must first identify himself and his location (i.e., the remote terminal he is using), and then authenticate his identification. The latter is essential if information files with limited access are requested. It is also desirable to avoid mischarging for computing costs. The identification-authentication steps may be repeated any number of times (e.g., when particularly sensitive files are requested).

Processing Restrictions

Although access control procedures can eliminate the simple threats from external sources, they cannot prevent sophisticated efforts nor completely counter legitimate users or system personnel inclined to browse. An infiltrator, once in the system will attempt to extract, alter, or destroy information in the files. Therefore, some processing restrictions (in addition to the normal information protection features) need to be imposed on files of sensitive information. For example, certain removable files may be mounted on input/output devices with read-only circuits, and alterations of data may be performed only after requests are authenticated by the controller of each file. Copying complete files (or large parts of files) is another activity where processing controls need to be imposed—again in the form of authentication by file controllers.

In systems where very sensitive information is handled, processing restrictions could be imposed on specific users in instances of "suspicious" behavior. For example, total cancellation of any query attempting to enter unauthorized files may be an effective countermeasure against browsing.

Threat Monitoring

Threat monitoring involves detection of attempted or actual penetrations of the system or files either to provide a real-time response (e.g., to invoke query cancellation, or to start tracing procedures) or to permit after the fact analysis. Threat monitoring may include recording of all rejected attempts to enter the system or specific files, use of illegal access procedures, unusual activity involving a certain file, attempts to write into protected files, attempts to perform restricted operations such as copying files, and excessively long periods of use. Periodic reports to users on file activity may reveal possible misuse or tampering and cause stepped-up auditing along with a possible real-time response. Such reports may range from a page synopsis of activity during the user session, to a monthly analysis and summary.

Privacy Transformations

Privacy transformations are techniques for coding the data in user-processor communications or in files to conceal information. They could be directed against passive (e.g., wiretapping) as well as sophisticated active threats (e.g., sharing a user's identification and communication link by a "piggy-back" infiltrator), and also afford protection to data in removable files against unauthorized access or physical loss.

A privacy transformation consists of a set of reversible logical operations on the individual characters of an information record, or on sets of such records. Reversibility is required to permit recovery (decoding) of the original information from the encoded form. Classes of privacy transformations include:

- Substitution—replacement of message characters with characters or groups of characters in the same or a different alphabet in a one-to-one manner (e.g., replacing alphanumeric characters with groups of binary numerals).

- Transposition—rearrangement of the ordering of characters in a message.

- Addition—using appropriate "algebra" to combine characters in the message with encoding sequences of characters (the "key") supplied by the user.

Well known among a number of privacy transformations of the "additive" type are the "Vigenere cipher," where a short sequence of characters is repeatedly used combined with the characters of the message. Another is the "Vernam system," where the user-provided sequence is at least as long as the message. Successive applications of several transformations may be used to increase the complexity.

In general, the user of a particular type of privacy transformation (say, the substitution of characters in the same alphabet) has a very large number of choices of transformations in that class. The identification of a particular transformation is the "key" chosen by the user for encoding the message. The same key is also necessary in the decoding of the message, and therefore must be available at both ends of the communications link.

From the hardware standpoint there exists equipment which provides automatic encoding/decoding. These include "scrambler" devices for voice-grade or low level data transmission, and devices such as Hagelin machines. The former are often used in law enforcement communication networks. Hagelin machines and their ilk are the standard means for transformation employed by government intelligence services.

As would be expected they are not inexpensive. The growth in information networks, however, suggests they will become rather economical devices.

Integrity Management

Important in providing privacy to an information system is verification that the system software and hardware perform as specified—including an exhaustive initial verification of the programs and hardware. For example, programs may be kept in locked cabinets equipped with alarm devices. Verification of the hardware and program or software integrity after each modification or repair should be a standard procedure, and inspection to detect changes of the emissive characteristics performed periodically.

Integrity of the communication channel is a far more serious problem and, if common carrier connections are employed, it will be extremely difficult to guarantee absence of wiretaps.

Personnel integrity (an essential element of privacy protection) poses some fundamental questions. The assumptions must be made that not everyone can be trusted. System privacy should be made to depend on the integrity of as few people as possible.

Section 3
System Aspects of Information Privacy

As pointed out previously, not all parts of an information system are equally vulnerable to threats to information privacy, and different countermeasures may be required in each part to counter the same level of threat. The structure and functions of the information processor, the programs, the files, and the communication network with terminals are sufficiently different to warrant separate discussion of information privacy with particular reference to these sub-systems.

Communication Lines and Terminals

Since terminals and communication channels are the principal user-to-processor links, privacy of information in this most vulnerable part of the system is essential.

Wiretapping

Multiple users spread over a wide area provide many opportunities for wiretapping. Since the cost of physically protected cables is prohibitive, there are no practical means available to prevent this form of entry. As a result, only through protective techniques applied at the terminals and at the processor can the range of threats from simple eavesdropping to sophisticated entry through special terminals be countered. While a properly designed password identification-authentication procedure is effective against some active threats, it does not provide a viable protection against the simplest threat—eavesdropping—nor against sophisticated "piggy-back" entry. The only broadly effective countermeasure appears to be the use of privacy transformations.

Radiation

In addition to the spectrum of threats arising from wiretapping, electromagnetic radiation from terminals must be considered. Every machine radiates electromagnetic energy because of the wires transmitting current, and magnetic and electrostatic fields are generated by these—they are all actually little transmitters.

Electromagnetic radiation characteristics will depend heavily on the type of terminal, and may in some cases pose serious shielding and electrical-filtering problems.

Obviously, the severity of these problems depends upon the physical security of the building or room in which the terminal is housed. Finally, proper handling and disposal of typewriter ribbons, carbon papers and used paper stock are essential.

Operating Modes

Whether it would be economical to combine both private and public modes of operation into a single user terminal is yet to be determined; but it appears desirable, perhaps even essential to permit a private terminal to operate in the public mode. However, the possibility of compromising the privacy system must be considered. For example, one can easily bypass any special purpose privacy software or hardware by throwing a switch manually. The program could be bypassed by computer. These controls, however, may become vulnerable to tampering. The engineering of the terminal must, therefore, assure reasonable physical, logical, and electrical integrity for a broad range of users and their privacy requirements.

Terminal Identification

An unambiguous and authenticated identification of a terminal is required to permit system initiated call-back for restarting or for "hang-up and re-dial" access control procedures. The need for authentication arises mainly when the terminal is connected to the processor via the common-carrier communication lines, where it is difficult to trace connections through the switching centers. If directly wired connections are used, neither authentication nor identification may be required, since (excluding wiretaps) only one terminal can be on a line.

Identification of a terminal could involve transmission of an internally (to the terminal) generated or user-entered code word consisting, for example, of two parts: one containing a description of the name of the terminal; the other, a password (more about these later) which authenticates that the particular terminal is in fact the one identified in the first part of the code word.

After terminal identification has been satisfactorily established, the processor may consult tables to determine the privacy level of the terminal; that is, the users admitted to the terminal and the protection techniques required.

User Identification

As with a terminal, identifying a user may require stating the user's name and account number, and then authenticating these with a password from a list.

If the security of this identification process is adequate, the normal terminal input mechanisms may be used; otherwise, special features will be required. For example, special equipment to accept and interpret coded cards might be employed, or sets of special dials or buttons provided. Procedures using the latter might consist of operating these devices in the correct sequence.

In some instances, if physical access to a terminal is appropriately controlled, terminal identification may be substituted for user identification.

Passwords

Clearly, a password authenticating a user or a terminal would not remain secure indefinitely. In fact, in an environment of potential wiretapping or radiative pickup, a password might be compromised by a single use. Employing lists of randomly selected passwords for "one-time-use", where a new word is taken from the list each time authentication is needed can be suggested as a countermeasure under such circumstances. One copy of such a list would be stored in the processor, the other maintained in the terminal or carried by the user. After signing in, the user would take the next word on the list, transmit it to the processor and then cross it off. The processor compares the received password with the next word in its own list and permits access only when the two agree. Such password lists could be stored in the terminal on punched paper tape, generated internally by special circuits, or printed on a strip of paper. The latter could be kept in a secure housing with only a single password visible. A special key lock would be used to advance the list. Since this method of password storage precludes automatic reading, the password must be entered using an appropriate input mechanism.

The protection provided by use of once-only passwords during sign-in procedures only is not adequate against more sophisticated "between lines" entry by an infiltrator who has attached a terminal to the legitimate user's line. Here the infiltrator can use his terminal to enter the system between communications from the legitimate user. In this situation the use of once-only passwords must be extended to each message generated by the user. Automatic generation and inclusion of authenticating passwords by the terminal would now be essential for smoothness of operation; and lists in the processor may have to be replaced by program or hardware implemented password generators.

Privacy Transformation

The identification procedures discussed above do not provide protection against passive threats through wiretapping, or against sophisticated "piggy-back" entry, as they are designed to render encoded messages unintelligible to all but holders of the correct key. Discovering the key, therefore, is essential for an infiltrator. The effort required to do this by analyzing intercepted encoded messages (rather than by trying to steal or buy the key) is the "work factor" of a privacy transformation. It depends greatly on the type of privacy transformations used, as well as on the knowledge and ingenuity of the infiltrator.

Another feature might allow the user to specify by appropriate statements whether privacy transforms are to be used or not. This would be part of a general set of "privacy instructions" provided in the information system operating programs. Each change from private to public mode, especially when initiated from the terminal, should be authenticated.

Files

While the privacy-protection techniques and access control procedures for external terminals and the communication network may greatly reduce the threat of infiltration by those with no legitimate access, they do not protect information against:

(1) legitimate users attempting to browse in unauthorized files,

(2) access by operating and maintenance personnel,

(3) physical acquisition of files by infiltrators.

A basic aspect of providing information privacy to files is the right of a user to total privacy of his files. Further, it should be possible to establish different levels of privacy in files. That is, it should be feasible to permit certain of a group of users to have access to all of the hospital's files, while allowing others limited access to only some of the files.

In this context certain standard file operations—such as file copying—would seem inappropriate, if permitted in an uncontrolled manner, since it would be easy to prepare a copy of a sensitive file and maintain it under one's own control for unauthorized purposes. Similarly, writing into files should be adequately controlled. For example, additions and deletions to certain files should be authorized only after proper authentication. It may even be desirable to mount some files on drives with physically disabled writing circuits.

Access Control of Files

Control of access to the files would be based on maintaining a list of authorized users for each file, where identification and authentication of identity, is established by the initial sign-in procedure. If additional protection is desired for a particular file, either another sign-in password or a specific file-access password is requested to reauthenticate the user's identity. The file-access passwords may be maintained in a separate list for each authorized user, or in a single list. If the latter, the system would ask the user for a password in a specific location in the list (e.g., the tenth password). Although a single list requires less storage and bookkeeping, it is inherently less secure. Protection of files is thus based on repeated use of the same requirements—identification and authentication—as for initial access to the system during sign in. This protection may be inadequate, however, in systems where privacy transformations are not used in the communication net (i.e., "piggy-back" infiltration is still possible).

Physical Vulnerability

An additional threat arises from possible physical access to files. In particular, the usual practice of maintaining backup files (copies of critical files for recovery in the case of drastic system failures) compounds this problem. Storage, transport, and preparation of these files all represent points of vulnerability for copying, theft, or an off-line print out. Clearly, possession of a reel of tape, for example, provides an interloper with the opportunity to peruse the information at his leisure. Applicable countermeasures are careful storage and transport, maintaining the physical integrity of files throughout the system, and the use of privacy transformations.

Privacy Transformations

At the terminals and in the communication network, privacy transformations could be used to protect files against failure of access control techniques or physical protection procedures. However, the engineering of privacy transformations for files differ considerably:

- Both the activity level and record lengths are considerably greater in files.

- Many users, rather than one, may share a file.

- Errors in file operations are more amenable to detection and control than those in communication links, and the uncorrected error rates are lower.

- More processing capability is available for the files, hence more sophisticated privacy transformations can be used.

- Many of the files may be relatively permanent and large, so that frequent changes of keys would be impractical due to the large amount of processing required.

It follows that the type of privacy transformation adequate for user-processor communications may be entirely unacceptable for the protection of files.

The choice of privacy transformations for an information file depends heavily on the amount of file activity in response to a typical information request, size and structure of the file (e.g., short records, many entry points), structure of the data within the file, and on the number of different users. Since each of these factors may differ from file to file, design of a privacy system must take into account the relevant parameters. For example, a continuous key for encoding an entire file may be impractical, as entry at intermediate points would be impossible. If a complex privacy transformation is desired additional parallel hardware may be required, since direct implementation by programming may unreasonably increase the processing time. In order to provide the necessary control and integrity of the transformation system, and to meet the processing time requirements, a simple, securely housed processor similar to a common input-output control unit might be used to implement the entire file control and privacy system.

The Processor

At any given moment in the system's operation the processor and its associated random-access storage units contain the basic threat monitoring program, system programs for various purposes as well as programs and data of currently serviced users. The role of the monitor is to provide the main line of defense against infiltration attempts through the software system by maintaining absolute control over all basic system programs for input-output, file access, user scheduling and privacy protection. It should also be able to do this under various contingencies such as system failures and recovery periods, debugging of system programs, and during start-up or shut-down of parts of the system. Clearly, the design of such a fail-safe monitor is a difficult problem.

Since it is unlikely that penetration attempts could be successfully attempted from outside the processor facility, protection relies mainly on adequate physical and personnel integrity. A first step is to keep the monitor in a read-only state, which can be altered only physically. It should be housed under lock and key. In fact, it would be desirable to embed the monitor into the basic hardware logic of the processor. Here, the hardware will perform the function in lieu of software.

Software integrity could be maintained by frequent comparisons of the current systems programs with carefully checked masters. Personnel integrity must, of course, be maintained at a very high level, and could be buttressed by team operation.

Integrity management procedures must be augmented with measures for controlling the necessary accesses to the privacy protection programs; or devices for insertion of passwords, keys, and authorization lists; or for maintenance. These may require the simultaneous identification and authentication of several of the information-center personnel (e.g., a system programmer and the center "privacy manager"), or the use of several combination locks for hardware-implemented privacy-protection devices.

Hierarchy of Privacy Protection

Privacy protection requires a hierarchy of system-operating and privacy-protection programs, with the primary system supervisor at the top. Under this structure, or embedded in it, may exist a number of similar but independent hierarchies of individual users' privacy-protection programs. It is neither necessary nor desirable to permit someone who may be authorized to enter this hierarchy at a particular level to automatically enter any lower level. Access should be permitted only on the basis of an authenticated "need to know." For example, if privacy transformations are employed by a particular user, his privacy programs should be protected against access by anyone.

Time-Sharing

Various modes of implementing time-sharing in the information system may affect the privacy of information in the processor. In particular, copying to back-up storage of residual information in active portions of core storage seems likely. This process would occur when a user's program has entered a suspended state, such as while waiting for a response from a terminal, and the storage space occupied by the program is required for another purpose. The contents of the core storage area occupied by the suspended program would be "swapped" for information or a program in immediate demand by the active state of the system—for example, another user's data. Upon completion of the "suspended" state—when he has made his response—the original user's program would be "swapped" back into the main core storage area. Since erasing all affected storage areas after each such time-period could be excessively time consuming, a reasonable solution may be to "tag" segments of information and programs as "private," or to set aside certain areas of core storage for private information and erase only those areas or core sectors after each time-period. Only the private core sectors would need to be erased as part of the swapping operation.

Also important is the effect of privacy transformations on processing time. Sophisticated privacy transformations, for example, may require a significant fraction of each time-period. It may be necessary, therefore, to use hardware implementation of privacy transformations by including these in the hardware versions of the monitor or through the use of a separate auxiliary processor for all communications control and privacy-transformation operations.

Hardware Failures

With respect to integrity management, there is one aspect of hardware integrity which is the responsibility of the original equipment manufacturer; a hardware failure should not be catastrophic in the sense that it would permit uncontrolled or even limited access to any part of the system normally protected. Whether this entails making the critical parts of the hardware totally reliable and infallible, or whether the system can be designed for a fail-safe form of graceful degradation is an open question. It is important to assure the user that the hardware has this basic characteristic. In addition, it may be necessary to maintain duplicate equipment for certain of the system processes; *e.g.* real-time monitoring functions.

These speculations are, of course, subject to modification, for each hospital must first determine its needs, design the total system, then purchase the equipment and obtain the personnel and finally write the programs including the safeguards and protective measures. An additional responsibility is that of educating relevant personnel from the medical, nursing and allied health staffs in how to use the system.

Of course, despite all precautions, safeguards and protective measures, information may still be disseminated to unauthorized persons. Therefore, the potential for liability must be discussed.

FOOTNOTE

[1]60 Ga. App. 92, 2 S.E.2d 810 (1939).

LIABILITIES

The question of liability for misuse of automated medical record systems must be answered on the basis of educated guesses at best. There are no cases on the point. Yet this conjectural approach is not at all idle speculation. The common law provides us with some clues as to how the courts may act in circumstances similar to those which may arise when automated medical record systems are employed in hospitals and harm results to the patient, through misuse or carelessness.

Two broad areas appear to be worthy of discussion. First, harm caused by unauthorized disclosure. Second, harm caused by carelessness with reference to the handling of information which comes from the computer.

To begin this discussion it is pertinent to note that hospitals may be liable because of duties imposed upon them as institutions. They may also be liable because of the wrong doing of their employees. These two approaches to liability are most often applied in cases dealing with negligence but they are applicable in all situations involving hospital liability. The first kind of liability comes about, as we have said, because of legal duties with which the institution, as an institution, must comply. The failure to meet the corporate responsibility will result in corporate liability. The second kind of liability comes about because of the doctrine of *respondeat superior,* which means, simply, that an employer is held responsible for the wrongful acts of its employees which result in harm to a third person.

With reference to unwarranted disclosure either the theory of corporate liability or *respondeat superior* may give rise to the imposition of liability on the hospital.

Section 1
Liability for Unwarranted Disclosure

Where information is revealed by a hospital without consent or justification two theories of liability appear to be available to a patient who can show harm. The patient may claim damages on a theory that he was defamed or he may sue on a theory of invasion of privacy. Where a physician has revealed information without justification, the patient may claim that a willful betrayal of professional secrets has occurred.

Defamation

Defamation may be defined as a written or oral communication, to someone other than the person defamed, of untrue matters concerning a living person which tend to injure his reputation. Under traditional concepts, libel was a written form of defamation while slander was oral, and libel was actionable without proof of actual damage. Certain types of slander, such as the imputation of crime or a loathsome disease, fell under the same rule, although ordinarily, special damages would have to be shown in order for oral publications to be actionable.

Medical records do contain information which, if published, would tend to affect a person's reputation in the community adversely. Thus, conceivably, disclosure by the hospital to an unauthorized person could result in an action for defamation. But that disclosure would have to contain untrue information.

In some cases the courts discuss a qualified privilege to disclose otherwise defamatory information where the author of the communication has an interest or a duty and where the communication is made to a person who has a corresponding interest or duty. Analysis of the cases indicate that liability will be imposed where there is conduct which can be shown to be unjustified. When truthful information is disclosed with good intention and for justifiable ends, the disclosure will not result in liability under either form of defamation. Release of information to interested parties would be protected by the above rule.

With reference to false information, such an an incorrect diagnosis, which may be in the record, it should be noted that only those publications which tend to diminish the esteem, respect, good will and confidence of the plaintiff in the community, or those publications which tend to excite adverse, derogatory or unpleasant feelings or opinions about the plaintiff are actionable. It seems unlikely that disclosures of inaccurate information concerning a man's medical status or treatment will be considered defamatory if the disclosure itself is justified.

In those instances where a hospital is serving its own interests, as in its efforts to procure payment from a third party, there can be no doubt that communications made in such circumstances are qualifiedly privileged since the hospital may be termed an interested party. Also, in those instances where a public interest is being served such as to protect the community, or a part thereof, from highly contagious diseases, it would seem proper to inform those persons interested of the relevant facts.

The situations above involve the conditional or qualified privilege. This privilege can be raised in situations when there are communications made in good faith, without actual malice with reasonable or probable grounds for believing them to be true, on a subject matter in which the author of the communication has an interest, or in respect to which he has a duty, public, personal, or private, either legal, judicial, political, moral, or social, made to a person having a corresponding interest or duty.

The law also recognizes an absolute privilege which applies to statements, otherwise defamatory, made in testimony, pleadings or other papers in judicial proceedings if such statements are material to the inquiry.

A more difficult question is presented when neither the interest of the hospital nor the general public is directly involved. Such cases may arise when there are requests by employers, insurance companies, newspapers, etc., for permission to examine or obtain information from hospital records. It is conceivable that in answering a private and confidential inquiry, the hospital is acting in the discharge of a legal, moral or social duty, and its answer may thus be qualifiedly privileged. This assumption has its basis in those cases which have held that when an apparently interested party makes a request for information concerning the general business character or credit of an individual, there is created a moral justification for disclosure because, under ordinary social standards, a reasonable man would feel called upon to speak.

By analogy, it can be theorized that disclosure of data in medical records to an employer, insurance company or to a party in litigation not involving the hospital may be qualifiedly privileged, since the interest of the community in securing justice would create a moral duty in the hospital to comply with such a request. Illustrative of this point is the holding that a qualified privilege attached to the response by an employer concerning a former servant with respect to an inquiry made by a prospective employer of the servant.[17]

The extent of the qualified privilege is uncertain and impossible to reduce to a formula. The publication must be justified by the importance of the interest served, and it must be called for by a legal or moral "duty", or by generally accepted standards of decent conduct.

A request for information from a totally disinterested person can never create a situation which is qualifiedly privileged. In order that a disclosure be privileged, the person to whom it is made must always have an interest. Whether or not the information was requested or volunteered will have some influence in determining whether the publisher acted in good faith or had a moral duty to communicate. A person is not precluded from volunteering information to an interested person when the communicant is serving his self interest or a community interest, or when there is an apparent legal or moral duty to speak, such as in a situation where a patient is attempting to defraud his insurance company, or a party he is suing. However, where none of these conditions is present, it would seem advisable to await a request by an interested person in order that there be created a moral duty to speak.

Invasion of Privacy

Many jurisdictions recognize the principle that an individual has the right to be protected from the mass dissemination of information pertaining to his personal, private affairs, and the unconsented to commercial use of his name, likeness or other personal matter. This right has been called the right of privacy. An invasion of this right is an unwarranted appropriation or exploitation of one's personality, the publicizing of one's private affairs with which the public has no legitimate concern, or a wrongful intrusion into one's private activities. To be actionable this invasion, exploitation, or intrusion must be done in such a manner as to cause outrage or mental suffering, shame or humiliation to a person of ordinary sensibilities.

It is possible that the release or disclosure of information in a medical record could lead to liability under this theory. However, the right of privacy is not an absolute right. The distinguishing characteristic of the right is that it is to protect the private citizen from mass dissemination of information concerning his private, personal affairs. It has also been said that oral publication cannot constitute an invasion of privacy, nor can the publication of data to an extent reasonably calculated to serve the legitimate interests of the publisher constitute such an invasion. Thus, the release or disclosure of information in the medical record to private individuals, such as attorneys, insurance company representatives or family members, would not ordinarily constitute an invasion of the right of privacy. The qualified and conditional privileges applicable in cases of defamation discussed above, apply to the right of privacy. It must further be remembered that the release, disclosure or publication must be of such a nature as to outrage or cause mental suffering, shame or humiliation to a person of ordinary sensibilities.

The right of privacy, generally, is the right of a private person to be kept out of the public spotlight. Thus, without more, it can be said that a disclosure of information from the medical record to private individuals could not be an invasion of a patient's right. In addition, this kind of publication may be privileged either absolutely, as in the case of statements made in court or before legislative and other official public bodies, or qualifiedly, as in the case of discharge of some public, private, legal or moral duty.

Perhaps the hospital practice most likely to give rise to questions of the invasion of privacy is the release of information concerning patients to news agencies. While the right of privacy does not prohibit disclosure of information which is of public or general interest, the extent of publication is still a matter to be weighed carefully by the hospital in each case.

Announcements of the admission or discharge of patients ordinarily pose no problem. However, the situation may be different where the hospital caters to specific diseases which are considered shameful in the popular mind. To publicize the fact that Mrs. Jones gave birth to a normal, healthy baby boy could not ordinarily be considered an overstepping of the bounds of propriety; but to publicize the fact that Mrs. Jones gave birth to a still-born monstrosity, or that Miss Brown had a child might be actionable.

The patient may be a public figure; his prominence, in itself, makes virtually all of his doings of interest to the public. Relatively obscure people may voluntarily take certain actions which will bring them before the public, or they may be victims of occurrences which are newsworthy, such as accidents, deliberate injuries, attempted suicides, police cases, etc., thus making the particular persons of interest to the public. The latitude extended to the publication of personal matters, names, photographs and the like varies as to these individuals. The public figure may not complain if his life is given some publicity, and this may be true long after he has ceased to be in the public eye. The ordinary citizen who voluntarily adopts a course of action which is newsworthy, cannot be heard to complain if the activity is reported along with his name and picture. However, as time passes the identity of the participant loses importance and an action for invasion of the right of privacy may then exist.

In the ordinary situation hospitals may release information of legitimate news value for immediate publication by news agencies without fear of a suit for invasion of the right of privacy. Nevertheless, hospital policy concerning the release of information to newspapers and other mass media should be formulated so that the interests of the patient are always protected.

Willful Betrayal of Professional Secrets

One final theory which might give rise to liability for the disclosure of information in the medical record without consent need only be mentioned in passing, because it mainly affects the activities of the physician, and is only tangentially applicable to hospitals. It is possible that release or disclosure of medical information might give rise to liability because it results in the betrayal of professional secrets to the detriment of the patient.

In a Nebraska case, *Simonsen v. Swenson*,[18] the plaintiff's physician informed the plaintiff's landlady that the plaintiff was suffering from a contagious disease. The landlady immediately forced the plaintiff to vacate the premises. Plaintiff sued the physician on the theory that a confidential communication had been revealed. The court held that the statute pertaining to confidential communications applied only to courtroom testimony, but pointed out that the statute relating to unprofessional conduct of physicians might have been applicable. This statute specifically identified the betrayal of professional secrets to the detriment of the patient as a cause for revocation of a doctor's license. The court, however, found that while, theoretically, civil liability might result, the act of the physician in this case was qualifiedly privileged, since the doctor had a "duty" to disclose the existence of the contagious disease to persons who might be affected. His disclosure to the landlady was thus privileged and he was not held liable to the patient.

In theory, if a licensing statute or regulation affecting hospitals were to prohibit the disclosure of confidential information concerning patients, and if the hospital violated that prohibition the hospital could be sued. However, the chance of liability under this theory is quite remote.

Section 2
Negligence and the Record

Aside from liability for unlawful disclosure of information in the medical records the hospital has to insure that the handling of information in an automated system provides for the same strict standards of accuracy and completeness that the handling of records in the manual system now requires. Moreover, even if the system is well run, the information in the record must be read carefully by those with a responsibility to provide direct patient care services. The liability may come about either under the doctrine of corporate negligence or *respondeat superior.* A few cases illustrate some possible examples of negligence.

In *Norton v. Argonaut Insurance Company,*[19] suit was brought against a nurse, a physician and the hospital's insurer for the wrongful death of a 3 month old girl. The nurse was held liable because she injected a fatal dose of medication without consulting the physician who made the order although she had doubts about the size of the dose as ordered. The hospital was held liable as the employer of the negligent nurse. The physician was held liable for negligently writing the dosage in the order sheet.

The pertinent facts were remarkably simple. They indicate how easy it is to fail to communicate in a large complex health-care organization. The infant had been receiving elixir pediatric lanoxin orally. The child's mother had been instructed by the physician to administer the medication. On the day the fatal dosage was administered, the physician instructed the mother to increase the daily dosage of lanoxin for that day only to 3.0cc instead of the usual 2.5cc. Following this instruction to the mother, the physician wrote on the order sheet the following instruction: "give 3.0cc lanoxin today for one dose only". The nurse, noting the doctor's orders and observing that there was no indication that it had been done, administered it in its injectable form instead of the elixir form which the doctor intended. The order as written did not indicate that the mother had already administered the medication.

The nurse believed the medication order was incorrect because of the dosage but she was not aware that the medication could be administered orally. She asked two physicians present in the ward whether she should give *the* medication as ordered by the attending physician. The other physicians did not interpret the order as the nurse did and, therefore, did not share her concern. They told her the attending physician's order did not appear out of line. The nurse did not obtain clarification from the attending physician and administered the medication according to her understanding of the order. At trial the medical evidence showed that 3.0cc of lanoxin administered to the infant by hypodermic was a lethal overdose and was the cause of the infant's death.

The court upheld the jury's finding that the nurse was negligent in that she failed to contact the attending physician before she gave the medication. The nurse was held liable as was the physician who wrote the ambiguous order that led to the fatal dose. The hospital was held liable under the doctrine of *respondeat superior.*

An automated system could contain built-in cross checks and signals to determine whether or not orders are written correctly. For example, a drug order would not be accepted as complete unless all variables such as form, route of administration and frequency of administration were specified by the physician. In a drug or medication identification process the name lanoxin might automatically produce its various forms including elixir pediatric. Moreover, before accepting the order, the doctor could be shown the complete order for review. In this case the computer could have determined from the choice of an elixir that the route of administration was oral and would so indicate. At the very least an automated system could remind the physician to indicate the route of administration in every case.

In the *Norton* case the appellate court's opinion indicates that the admission form stated that the mother had been instructed to administer the medication. An integrated automated system could possibly have made that information available to the nurse.

An automated information system no matter how simple or sophisticated will only be effective if the persons responsible for using the information use it carefully. This means that the input must be accurate and that the output must be read and understood. This is true in manual as well as automated systems.

The case of *Larrimore v. Homeopathic Hospital Assn. of Delaware,*[20] concerned a male patient who had been receiving a drug by injection over a period of time. The attending physician wrote an order changing the mode of administration from injection to oral. When the nurse on the unit, who had been off duty for several days, was preparing to give the medication to the patient by injection, the patient objected and referred the nurse to the physician's new order. Although the nurse claimed that she reviewed the patient's record, she gave the medication by injection, after telling the patient he was mistaken. Either the nurse had not reviewed the order sheet or she did so carelessly and did not note the physician's entry. The failure was found to be negligence and the nurse and the hospital (under *respondeat superior*) were liable. The most accurate medical record system possible will not be effective unless those who have the responsibility to read and evaluate the information do so with care.

In *Favalora v. Aetna Casualty & Surety Company*,[21] the failure of a radiologist and employees of a hospital to refer to the patient's medical record before commencing a radiological examination was the basis of liability. The patient, a 71 year old woman, had been advised by her family physician to enter the hospital for diagnostic study because she complained of weight loss, pain in her stomach, and an episode of fainting. On the morning following her admission she was taken to the radiology department for X-ray studies ordered by the family physician. The hospital's requisition form for X-rays, completed by a nurse, did not mention her medical history, as it was the customary procedure in the hospital to fill in the medical history portion of the requisition only for cardiac patients or those who were bleeding. The radiologist, assisted by a hospital technician, instructed the patient to step forward upon the footboard of the X-ray table which was then in a vertical position. The patient fainted and fell to the floor after the room light had been turned off and a fluoroscope examination had been initiated. Neither the radiologist nor the technician was aware of any evidence of distress prior to the patient's fall.

Although the footboard of the X-ray table was only one and one half inches from the floor, the patient sustained a fractured hip from the fall requiring an open reduction, which in turn aggravated a pre-existing vascular disorder causing a pulmonary embolism, necessitating additional surgery, followed by a kidney infection. The patient recovered money damages in her law suit against the radiologist and the hospital and their liability insurers.

The court held that the radiologist acted negligently in failing to acquaint himself with the patient's history before commencing his examination and further that he was negligent in failing to anticipate the possibility of a patient fainting regardless of age or physical condition. The court reasoned that if the history had been obtained and consulted it would have disclosed the prior fainting episodes and would have prompted increased alertness on the part of the radiologist and technician.

In addition to finding the radiologist negligent, the court also imposed liability upon the hospital. The twofold basis of the hospital's liability was the failure of the nurse responsible for completing the X-ray requisition to secure and include the patient's medical history and the failure of the X-ray technician to anticipate the possibility of a patient fainting during the course of examination.

This decision illustrates the significant role the medical record can play in litigation, but more importantly, it highlights the necessity for the proper use by hospital personnel of the medical history in the treatment and care of patients.

Once again an automated medical record information system could be designed to generate the necessary background information to the departments, laboratories and services which are supportive of direct patient care. A routine set of information notations could be prepared and generated with each requisition for services such as X-ray, physical therapy, blood and the like. Such a system would have to have built-in protections against the kinds of errors discussed above.

Moreover, protections would have to be developed to prevent system error. That is, the automated system itself should be so devised that the processing of information does not inject new errors. These errors fall into several categories. The machine itself, due to some malfunction, may delete information or add extraneous information. The machine may misread or misprint information. Thus, for example, "0.3" could be transformed into "3.0" or even "30.". Of course, technicians and input personnel would have to be trained to act with the highest degree of care at all times. When we remember that some part of the communication of medical information may be oral (later to be transcribed and authenticated) it will be necessary to develop a set of checks and confirmations of orders before they are input into the machine. While there is no attempt here to create imaginary problems, there is the possibility of increased liability precisely because automated equipment is used.

In *Ball Memorial Hospital v. Freeman*,[22] liability derived from control of the instrumentality causing harm was discussed in terms that could apply with reference to the use of automated devices in hospitals where something harmful occurs. In the case itself one question was the application of the doctrine of *res ipsa loquitur* ("the thing speaks for itself") to situations where patients are harmed by a medication prepared by hospital personnel.

The patient had an operation to remove a loose cartilage from a joint of his left thumb. In the course of the operation a fluid supposedly a novocaine anesthetic, was injected into the thumb. The fluid was in fact a poisonous and deleterious substance. It was prepared, placed in a container, stored and delivered by hospital employees. At all times the medication was under the control of the hospital. The injection of the fluid caused great pain and swelling to the patient's hand and arm and caused an ulcer at the base of the patient's thumb necessitating skin graft operations and the removal of a nerve.

The court held that the hospital was liable under the principle of corporate negligence for failing to employ proper instruments and facilities in preparing, bottling and dispensing drugs. The court said that the doctrine of *res ipsa loquitur* was applicable to this case. The court went on to say, in a footnote:

> The use of automation devices in modern hospitals such as for monitoring patient's temperature, pulse and respiration is today an accomplished fact.

And then in the body of the opinion the court said:

> As complicated mechanical devices of our modern age achieve greater perfection and greater reliance upon them is justified, it follows that the doctrine [*res ipsa loquitur*] has a broader application than originally.

The principle enunciated in the *Freeman* case can be applied to the use of automated information retrieval systems. The failure to operate or the introduction of incorrect information, either of which causes harm to the patient, could shift the burden of proof from the plaintiff to the defendant.

The doctrine of *res ipsa loquitur* applies in cases where the plaintiff alleges negligence but cannot, because of the nature of the occurrence, present proof of carelessness. Three conditions are necessary for the doctrine to apply. The circumstances must be such that harm would not have occurred but for the negligence of someone; the instrument, device or object causing the harm was under the control of the defendant, and the plaintiff did nothing to contribute to the harm.

Because so much of the delivery of medical care depends on accurate and complete information, the individuals who are charged with responsibility to interpret and act upon such information must perform with a degree of care commensurate with the danger which will be caused by inaccurate, incomplete or misleading medical recordings. Thus, whether or not the doctrine of *res ipsa loquitur* will apply in those situations involving automated medical records, the physicians, nurses and other health personnel are under a continuing duty of care. No one can rely on a machine output merely because it is a machine output.

Negligence is proved by showing that the defendant has failed to meet a standard of care. The standard of care is a measure by which the actions of the defendant are compared with a hypothetical reasonably prudent person acting under similar circumstances. In the past the standard of care was determined by reviewing what was the usual practice in the same or similar communities. Today that rule is changing both as to institutions and individuals.

In *Darling v. Charleston Memorial Hospital*,[23] perhaps the most important recent case in hospital law, the Illinois Supreme Court rejected the community rule. The court indicated that it would look to the rules and regulations promulgated by governmental agencies, the standards of the Joint Commission on Accreditation of Hospitals and the hospital's own by-laws and regulations to determine the standard of care. In short, a multi-regional or even national standard of care may be evolving. The same may be said for the standard of care in cases against physicians alleging malpractice. As the Massachusetts Supreme Judicial Court said in *Brune v. Belinkoff*,[24]

> "We are of the opinion that the locality rule ... which measures a physician's conduct by the standards of other doctors in similar communities is unsuited to present day conditions. The time has come when the medical profession should no longer be 'balkanized' by the application of varying geographic standards in malpractice cases."

In the *Brune* case the plaintiff was delivered of a baby. During the delivery, the defendant doctor, a specialist in anesthesiology practicing in New Bedford, administered a spinal anesthetic to the plaintiff containing 8 mg. of pontocaine in one cubic centimeter of 10 percent glucose solution. When the plaintiff attempted to get out of bed eleven hours later, she slipped and fell on the floor. She subsequently complained of numbness and weakness in her left leg, an affliction which persisted for some time. Testimony was given by eight physicians. Much of it related to the plaintiff's condition. There was ample medical evidence that the 8 mg. dosage was excessive and that good medical practice required a dosage of 5 mg. or less. The practice in New Bedford was to give the 8 mg. dosage. The practice in Boston was to give 5 mg. The appellate court found that the standard to be followed was that of the physicians in Boston. Standards of care change as medical practice changes.

There is a line of cases which hold that nurses are under a duty to question a physician's orders or actions when it is apparent that they are contrary to normal practice and procedures. If the physician does not respond to such affirmative questions, the nurses have a duty to alert someone in authority. *Darling v. Charleston Memorial Hospital,* discussed above, makes this point.

The burden of maintaining an awareness of the literature in the field, of staying alert to new findings and results of continuing experimentation, is a heavy one. Yet, the courts will more easily define a duty to be obeyed today than ever before. Automation and biomedical instrumentation require an alertness that is precise and pervasive and that duty of awareness is all the more important precisely because of a natural tendency to rely on the computer's authoritative output. Moreover, because the new technology requires a precision heretofore unknown, it may be that the required clarity and explicitness exceeds the capability of the ordinary prudent doctor or nurse. One cannot tell.

Applying the principles of negligence to medical automation generally and medical record automation specifically, it appears that the hospital planning to employ the modern devices, machines, instruments and techniques must be aware of current standards of practice. This is not to say that hospitals must use the latest equipment or be found to be negligent. It is to say that if automation is employed in the hospital it must be done with due care. It must be used with full awareness of the safeguards and protective measures recognized to be necessary in order to take full advantage of what may be called progress while at the same time protecting the patient.

Liability, then, may flow from the use of medical record automation if harm results to a patient or others either as a result of unwarranted disclosures or because of careless handling of the equipment or the information it provides.

FOOTNOTES

[17]Doane v. Grew, 220 Mass. 171, 107 N.E. 620 (1915).

[18]104 Neb. 224, 177 N.W. 831 (1920).

[19]144 So.2d 249 (La. App. 1962).

[20]54 Del. 449, 181 A.2d 573 (1962).

[21]144 So.2d 544 (La. App. 1962).

[22]245 Ind. 71, 196 N.E.2d 274 (1964).

[23]33 Ill.2d 326, 211 N.E.2d 253 (1965).

[24]235 N.E.2d 793 (1968).

THE MEDICAL RECORD IN COURT

The increasing incidence of personal injury litigation and the expanding use of life, accident and health insurance are major factors which operate to make medical records important evidentiary documents. Specific factual data related to medical diagnosis, treatment and prognosis are found in no other place in such an organized form. The need to prove such data in court increases. However, there is some diversity of opinion as to the admissibility of medical records or parts of medical records, in judicial proceedings.

As a general rule courts receive into evidence the sworn testimony of witnesses who are subject to cross examination by the opposing attorneys and occasionally the questions of the trial judge. Statements which are not sworn to or subject to cross examination are not admissible because they are one form of hearsay. Clearly, the medical record is hearsay because it contains unsworn statements made outside of the courtroom at some time in the past and offered at trial to prove the facts it reflects. The information in the record must also be relevant to the issues in the trial. If it is not, such information will not be admitted into evidence. In some states, medical opinions and conclusions and other material in the record which is not factual in nature will not be admitted. Of course, the physician who wrote the opinion or made the conclusion can testify as a witness.

Thus, whether or not medical information will be accepted into evidence at trial depends upon a number of factors and the specific rules of court procedure in the various state and federal trial courts.

Records are also subject to subpoena in legal proceedings which occur before the actual trial. In these pre-trial proceedings, counsel for either side may obtain information by the legal processes of discovery and examination before trial. Some statutes and rules provide for an examination based on written interrogatories. In all states there is some method of requiring the production of documents relating to the litigation. In pre-trial proceedings information may be obtained which would not be admissible at trial.

Section 1
Proving the Record

There are recognized exceptions to the hearsay rule, and, as indicated previously, the privileged communications statutes vary considerably from state to state, not only as to the scope of coverage but also as to the manner in which the patient may be deemed to have waived his privilege.

101

Privileged communications statutes aside, the medical record may be admitted into evidence if it can be shown that it was prepared in the "regular course of business" of the hospital. The manually created record is admissible so long as the court can assure itself that the information was routinely gathered in the course of the business of the institution (that is, not created specially for the purpose of trial), was recorded at or near the time the event took place and is trustworthy.

When a record of this nature is to be admitted into evidence the custodian of the record will testify as to the manner in which the record was created, maintained and protected. From this testimony the court is able to determine whether or not the safeguards and guarantees of trustworthiness are fulfilled.

Hospital records are admitted into evidence on a variety of grounds. In states where, by statute, records are required to be kept by certain hospitals, such documents, including medical records, may be admitted under the exception to the hearsay rule relating to public or official records and they are admissible under workmen's compensation and lien laws.

In other states, medical records are admissible where it can be shown that they are made in the regular course of business. The Uniform Business Records as Evidence Act has been adopted by a large number of states, while several have adopted a Model Act which also provides for the admissibility of records made in the regular course of business.

In those states which have adopted neither the Uniform nor the Model Act, medical records may, nevertheless, be admissible. In some states the common law "shop book rule" permits the introduction of such evidence. In Florida, hospital records have been admitted as public records. Of course, these records must meet the usual evidentiary tests of relevancy and materiality. That is, the information must relate to the issue for which it is being introduced. It must be of substance and have some weight—it must not be immaterial.

However, having met these tests, the introduction of medical records may still be objected to on the ground that the matter contained therein is information subject to the operation of the physician-patient confidential communication statute. Although these statutes have been held to apply to confidential matters appearing in medical records, they will affect the hospital directly only in those cases in which the hospital is a party. In suits between the patient and others where records have been subpoenaed it is not the hospital's concern or right to assert or deny the privilege when the records are subpoenaed. This problem is for the courts and parties in the suit. In those cases involving hospitals, the privilege will be effective only as to matters in certain types of causes, if it cannot be shown that the patient has waived (given up) his privilege.

The hearsay and confidential communications rules, as they apply to medical records, do not affect the use of hospital records in non-judicial situations. While these considerations are of importance, other factors come into play in determining what matters may be disclosed out-of-court without legal repercussions.

An important question with reference to admissibility of records contained in an automated library or repository is that of authentication, or more precisely, trustworthiness. When the custodian of a manually created record testifies as to the manner in which individuals physically placed words, notes and signatures on paper and how that paper was then stored and protected, his testimony is easily understood by the judge and jury. But testimony about computers and retrieval of information is a different matter. The general public is not yet familiar—or comfortable—with concepts and practices of automated data processing. Thus, care must be taken to describe in some detail the steps involved in the development of the automated medical record information system so that the court, the jury and counsel understand its nature and what it can do. Although no cases have yet been found dealing directly with the question of admissibility of automated hospital records, several cases on admissibility of automated business records, spell out the procedures to be followed at the time the automated record is to be introduced into evidence.

In *Transport Indemnity Company v. Seib,*[25] an action by an insurance company to recover premiums earned under an insurance contract, the principal issue was the admission into evidence of an exhibit which was a printout of business information which was stored on magnetic tape. The court held that the testimony of the insurance company's director of accounting describing how the record (of claims paid on behalf of the insured and gross receipts of the business) was made and stored on tape by electronic equipment and how information relating to the total amount of premiums earned under the contract was computed, laid the proper foundation for admission of the record produced by the computer. With reference to the machine processing of such information the court said:

> The machine here performs the bookkeeping task in the usual course of business. Instead of on paper, the information and calculations are stored on tape and may be retrieved and printed at any time. The tape record furnished a cumulative record based on information flowing into the office of the plaintiff company day by day and fed into the machine in response to a systematic procedure for processing each insured's account.

The court held that the testimony to establish the trustworthiness of the records followed the state's business records as evidence statute and that therefore the admission of the computer-generated evidence in the trial court was correct.

This case, while indicating that the printout of part of the magnetic tape file may be admissible into evidence, providing the proper foundation is laid, raises an additional question. Traditionally, the medical record librarian or an employee of the library carried the records to court in response to the *subpoena duces tecum.* In the case of an automated medical information system, it may be that the person who supervises the data processing system will have to accompany the printout of the record to court and testify as to the procedures followed in creating, storing, retrieving and safeguarding the information which is brought to court in a printout reproduction of the tape (or other storage media).

In any event the information will speak for itself, that is, it will be admitted into evidence or rejected from evidence on the general rules applicable to admissibility. The custodian of the record, whether medical record librarian or manager of the machine processing unit, has the primary responsibility of providing information to the court to show that this is an authentic business record of the institution. (As an interesting sidelight to the *Seib* case, the court indicated that the testimony of the manager of the data processing division covered 141 pages of the trial record).

It must be emphasized that the court will be concerned with the authenticity, the reliability and the trustworthiness of the information it is allowing into the trial record. Thus, the witness who testifies about the system should come prepared to describe to the court the routines and procedures for reporting, storing, retrieving and safeguarding the information in the automated system.

Although the cases are few there seems no question that courts will admit into evidence computer-generated information which is relevant and material. They will undoubtedly liberally interpret not only statutes such as the Uniform Business Records as Evidence Act but also the common law "shop book rule".

In *Matthews Estate,*[26] an insurance company claimed moneys due from the estate of a deceased agent. To sustain the claim the company offered in evidence a computer printout from a magnetic tape record indicating the amounts due. The court ruled in favor of receiving the evidence and allowed the claim. The court said:

> We believe that the Uniform Business Records as Evidence Act makes print-outs of electronically-produced record tapes admissible in evidence if the testimony of the custodian of the record, or of a person familiar with the system under which the record is prepared testifies in support of it that the record

was prepared in accordance with the requirements of the said Act.

It is to be noted that the court in the *Matthews* case upheld the admissibility of computer records at least three processing stages removed from the original record. The deceased agent had issued insurance policies and prepared daily reports. A copy of the daily report (most likely the original record) went to the regional office where it was coded and abstracted by one department. The information was placed on machine-readable cards by another department and the cards were processed so as to create the tape from which the printout was obtained in the computer center. While the Uniform Act allows copies of the original records to be placed in evidence, at one time the common law "shop book rule" only allowed the introduction of the original record. However, this rule now appears to be modified even with reference to automated records.

In *King v. State ex rel. Murdock Acceptance Corporation*[27] the Supreme Court of Mississippi held that the "shop book rule" would not prevent the admissibility of computer-generated information so long as safeguards were shown to have been followed. The court stated:

> Records stored on magnetic tape by data processing machines are unavailable and useless except by means of the print-out sheet such as those admitted in evidence in this case. In admitting the print-out sheets reflecting the record stored on the tape, the Court is actually following the best evidence rule. We are not departing from the shop book rule, but only extending its application to electronic record keeping.

> In sum, we hold that print-out sheets of business records stored on electronic computing equipment are admissible in evidence if relevant and material, without the necessity of identifying, locating, and producing as witnesses the individuals who made the entries in the regular course of business if it is shown (1) that the electronic computing equipment is recognized as standard equipment, (2) the entries are made in the regular course of business at or reasonably near the time of the happening of the event recorded, and (3) the foundation testimony satisfies the court that the sources of information, method and time of preparation were such as to indicate its trustworthiness and justify its admission.

We are not to be understood as indicating that computer evidence is infallible. Its probative value is the same as conventional books, and it is subject to refutation to the same extent.

As the Mississippi court indicated computer evidence is not infallible, and certainly the printout of an automated medical record will be subject to the objections that can be made against a manually created record. The Arizona court in *Kemp v. Pinal County*[28] refused to admit the results of a blood alcohol test from an autopsy report on the grounds that it was made neither in the routine course of business nor near the time of the event (the decedent's death). *Neas v. Snapp*[29] rejected records in a similar fact situation because the qualifications of the physician who made the test were not established.

With regard to admissibility of an automated record into the trial it can be concluded that the court and contending counsel will settle questions relating to the contents of medical records. But at the pre-trial stage, in discovery proceedings different rules may apply.

Section 2
Pre-trial Examinations

Long before a trial begins the lawyer for each side has investigated the facts, researched the law and prepared his case in the best possible way. In many states a pre-trial conference may be called by the judge on his own initiative or at the request of any party. This conference is intended to be a discussion between the judge and the attorneys to eliminate matters which are not in dispute, to agree on the issues to be determined at trial, and clearing up matters of procedure. Sometimes cases are settled at this point.

In the federal courts and in many state courts, the parties have a right to conduct examinations before trial. In some states this procedure is called discovery. Either party may question the other side under oath, and third persons as well. The reason for discovery is to permit each side to learn what the opponent knows. The trial can then proceed in an orderly and logical fashion with disputed matters properly presented and argued. A party may send a questionnaire to the other party asking him any questions about the facts of the case. These are called interrogatories. He may require the other parties and witnesses to appear before an examiner and answer under oath what they know about the case. These sworn statements are called depositions. Either party may obtain subpoenas permitting examination of books, papers and records.

A growing majority of courts which have spoken on this question have allowed plaintiffs in malpractice actions quite liberal discovery. If the plaintiff can show that the information sought is relevant to the subject matter of the case or reasonably calculated to lead to the discovery of admissible evidence he is on solid ground. There is a recognition by the courts of the plaintiff's difficulty in discovering evidence in a malpractice action. Relevant facts and information are likely to be in the sole possession of the physician and his colleagues or in hospital records other than patient medical records.

For instance, in *Myers v. St. Francis Hospital*,[30] the plaintiff brought a malpractice action against a hospital and a physician for an alleged negligent blood exchange transfusion administered to an infant. The court entered an order directing the physician to answer certain interrogatories. The physician appealed the order but the appellate court held that it was proper and relevant to inquire of the defendant what he did, and why, and what happened in the course of or as a result of the procedures he followed. Moreover, the plaintiff was held to be entitled to have questions answered which sought information as to the physician's qualifications, experience and treatment in similar cases.

The New Jersey court in this case stressed the fact that the rules permitting discovery of any matter (1) relevant to the subject matter of the pending action or (2) reasonably calculated to lead to the discovery of admissible evidence, were designed to encourage full discovery of all matters not irrelevant or privileged. Thus, questions relating to the physician's license, education and internship, training and experience in a specialty, hospital connections, teaching, membership in medical societies, writings, and occasions on which he performed similar treatments (as well as the names, addresses, dates and factual accounts of every patient for whom he performed a similar procedure) had to be answered. The court said this information related to the physician's qualification and experience and were proper matters for cross-examination.

Importantly, the *Myers* case points to a trend on the part of the courts to allow discovery of not only admissible evidence but also information which will enable a party to prepare for trial effectively. Several other cases also highlight this trend.

In *Kenney v. Superior Court*,[31] a patient was allowed to subpoena the records of a hospital relating to the defendant doctor. The records sought by the plaintiff dealt with disciplinary proceedings, if any, held against the doctor, the doctor's status on the hospital staff and any indication of his removal from the staff. The trial court ordered the production of those records because they might have discovery value and might assist the plaintiff in his preparation for trial. The appellate court agreed stating:

> "Records of disciplinary proceedings, or of the status of a
> doctor on a hospital staff, or of his removal therefrom, may
> or may not be admissible evidence. Even if inadmissible such

records may very well point the way to evidence admissible in a medical malpractice action."

The court also required the defendant to answer certain interrogatories about facts indicating whether or not he had conferred with experts pertaining to any facts dealing with the medical care, treatment, prognosis or diagnosis of the plaintiff. In the event of an affirmative answer the interrogatory required the disclosure of the names, addresses, and specialties of such experts and the dates of contact. The defendant was also asked to disclose whether or not any experts were to be called as witnesses, if so the same information with reference to names, addresses and specialties was sought. The appellate court ruled that the question relating to the conference with experts pertaining to the facts and statistical information about the patient as well as the names, addresses and specialization of such experts was proper and had to be answered. The court also held that the defendant had to disclose the names of any witnesses he intended to call.

Finally, the defendant was asked to disclose whether the factors relating to the case had been presented to a medical committee, and if an affirmative answer was made, to disclose the dates and places of conferences, names and addresses and telephone numbers and type or class of doctors that were on the committee. The court held that the defendant was not required to disclose the names, addresses and information about the medical committee. It said that requiring this disclosure would be a violation of the "work product" privilege. This privilege will be discussed more fully shortly.

In the *Kenney* case, it is of interest to note that there was a standing hospital rule against the release of records without a court order. Thus, the plaintiff in addition to presenting sufficient information in court to justify the issuance of the subpoena also claimed that he had no access to any of the information while the defendant would either have access to the records or would have knowledge of their contents.

Under many modern statutes and court rules, private documents of all kinds are subject to discovery and examination prior to trial so long as it can be shown that they are pertinent and material to the issues in the case. As the *Myers* and *Kenney* cases show, information from private documents, such as hospital records, can be discovered not only when they relate to the issues in the case but also when they are relevant to the subject matter and when they will assist the party in his preparation for trial. Even where documents are specifically made inadmissible, they may still be subject to discovery.

The breadth of the *Kenney* decision may be narrowed, however, by a 1968 amendment to the California Evidence Code. This statute removes from the zone of discoverable information the proceedings and records of organized committees of hospital medical staffs having the responsibility of evaluation and improvement of the quality of the care rendered. The proceedings of medical review committees of local medical societies are also covered. With certain exceptions, no person in attendance at a meeting of such committee shall be required to testify as to what transpired.

Another California statute provides that the written records of interviews, reports, statements or memoranda of in-hospital medical staff committees relating to research and medical studies for the purpose of reducing morbidity or mortality are not admissible in evidence. The statute further provides that the disclosure with or without the consent of the patient, of information concerning him to such in-hospital medical staff committees does not make unprivileged information which would otherwise be privileged. These data are, however, subject to discovery proceedings, except that the identity of any patient may not be discovered unless the patient consents to such disclosure. The admissibility into evidence of the original medical records of any patient is not affected by this act.

In an automated record system many hospital records in addition to patient records may also be maintained. These it would seem are subject to subpoena and to discovery under pre-trial examination even though they may or may not be admissible in the actual trial. However, some of the hospital records which are specially prepared may not be subject to subpoena or discovery.

Section 3
Incident Reports

Incident reports are special kinds of reports. They may be routinely made and kept by the hospital or they may be made only when a major incident occurs and then sent to hospital counsel. We are now discussing the incident report which is an in-depth evaluation of an untoward occurrence in the hospital. Not included are the routine factual reports which are placed in the patient's record. If incident reports are routinely made as part of the hospital's record keeping system, they may be subject to review upon subpoena because they are hospital records. But if incident reports are specially prepared for use by hospital insurers or attorneys, other lawyers may not be able to obtain the information. A ruling from California holds, to some degree at least, that specially prepared incident reports are not to be made available to patient's counsel.

In *Sierra Vista Hospital v. Superior Court*[32] a California District Court of Appeals prohibited a lower court from enforcing an order that directed the hospital to make available, for inspection by the patient's attorney, the incident report prepared by the nursing service director and hospital administrator. The report in question was prepared for the confidential use of the hospital's insurer, and no copy was retained in the hospital. The court held that the hospital, like a private person, is entitled to the protection of the attorney-client privilege, and that the report was in the nature of a confidential communication from the hospital corporation to its attorney, through the insurance company. The information was considered to be part of the "work product" of the attorney and therefore protected by the attorney-client privilege.

On the other hand, *Bernardi v. Community Hospital Association*[33] held that incident reports were subject to discovery proceedings. In this case the reports were prepared by a nurse who was alleged to have been negligent in administering an injection. She placed the report in the patient's chart, and copies were given to the hospital administrator and the director of nurses. They were not, the evidence showed, prepared exclusively for the hospital's attorney and the court held that they could not be protected against discovery. The Colorado court said:

> "It may well be that the practice of making an incident report resulted from the advice of counsel, but it seems rather plain that these incident reports were not prepared for the attorney. Rather, they were prepared for certain administrative officials of the hospital and they were available to the hospital's attorney if he wished to see them. To entitle the party to the protection accorded privileged communications, the communication must be made to the counsel, attorney, or solicitor acting for the time being, in character of legal advisor, and must be made by the client for the purpose of professional advice in aid upon the subject of his rights and liabilities."

This is not to suggest that incident reports should not be kept. There are strong reasons for having them written at the time an incident occurs because the memories of witnesses and participants are then still fresh, and more of the facts can be obtained. A periodic review and analysis of the incident reports can lead to corrective measures that will be of benefit to the hospital as well as its patients.

Although many seem to think otherwise, the incident report is not an indictment and will not necessarily lead to a conclusion that the hospital is or was negligent. On the contrary, it may show quite clearly that the patient was careless. It may show that the occurrence was an unavoidable accident for which no one will be liable under a theory of negligence. The possibility of a law suit, however, is ever-present even if the outcome is favorable to the hospital. Suit itself is time-consuming and costly.

An automated record system with retrieval capabilities could alert the administrator to those areas, individuals or activities in the hospital which show frequent incidents. The report, if used correctly and acted upon could be a major management tool. Yet there are dangers. In the final analysis, the decision to maintain a routine incident reporting system is an administrative one based on the advice and guidance of the hospital's counsel. The decision to maintain an automated file on these reports should be made after the initial decision is made to maintain the reports routinely.

A related question which has arisen is whether the report of the tissue committee of the medical staff is admissible. This report is not a medical record but it may relate to the care and treatment of an individual patient. In *Judd v. Park Avenue Hospital*[34] a patient sought to subpoena the records of "any and all medical staff discussions and meetings of committees" relative to the surgery performed upon him. The court refused to allow the subpoena. It held that the statements were hearsay; such reports were distinguished from entries in the patient's records made contemporaneously with his treatment. The patient also sought to examine entries in the surgical log book and entries in the operations records and disease index cards relating to surgery performed by the defendant physicians prior to the time of plaintiff's treatment. The court held that only those entries in the surgical log book relating to treatment of the plaintiff could be examined and the entries in the operations records and disease index could not be examined because they were privileged information about the treatment of other patients.

The medical record will grow in importance as medical and nursing practice become more sophisticated. At some time in the not too distant future the medical record will contain an encyclopedic reference about a patient. It will be complete and precise and subject not only to instantaneous searching, retrieval and analysis for a multiplicity of medical purposes but also it will be subject to discovery and subpoena by lawyers representing litigants. If the attorney represents the patient he *should* have access to the information concerning his client in printout form or otherwise. If the attorney represents the hospital he will have access to the information because his client can use the information in its defense. If the attorney represents third parties such as governmental agencies, insurers and others with a legally recognized interest, he may or may not have access depending upon his showing of a legitimate reason for seeing the information.

FOOTNOTES

[25] 178 Neb. 253, 132 N.W.2d 871 (1965).

[26] 117 Pitts. Leg. Journal 223 (Orphan's Ct. Alleg. County, Pa. 1969).

[27] 222 So.2d 393 (Miss. 1969).

[28] 8 Ariz. App. 41, 442 P.2d 864 (1968).

[29] 221 Tenn. 325, 426 S.W.2d 498 (1968).

[30] 91 N.J. Super. 377, 220 A.2d 693 (1966).

[31] 255 Cal. App.2d 106, 63 Cal. Rptr. 84 (1967).

[32] 248 Cal. App.2d 359, 56 Cal. Rptr. 387 (1967).

[33] 443 P.2d 708 (Colo. 1968).

[34] 37 Misc.2d 614, 235 N.Y. Supp.2d 843 (Sup. Ct. 1962), *aff'd*, 18 App. Div.2d 766, 235 N.Y. Supp. 1023 (1962).

BRINGING ABOUT CHANGE

This discussion and analysis did not aim to portray a gallery of imaginary fears and horribles. There definitely are statutes, regulations, and judicial concepts which clearly inhibit the installation of an automated medical record information system as a total replacement to the present manual system.

As this book suggests, some of these legal restrictions can be changed immediately. Some legal impediments may be changed but only after careful evaluation of the implications of such modification. Other regulations should not be changed because they ensure that the medical record will be safe and reliable.

The primary thrust for change in the law will have to come from the physicians, medical record librarians, administrators, manufacturers and systems engineers who are in this instance the promoters of progress and the need for change. These individuals and organizations have a vital responsibility to aid and inform the law makers so that they can comprehend and meet the challenge of change. With proper information the law will support and enhance the transition from the medical systems we now know to the new medicine. The law will at the same time continue to protect the public health, safety and welfare.

With the law's mission in mind but remembering the ways in which some technological changes have modified our lives for "better or for worse", we should maintain a cautious optimism about the automation of medical records.

The implementation of such a system should proceed at a pace which allows time for testing and evaluation of its impact on the primary business of hospitals, that of providing high quality medical and hospital care. Thus, it is not enough to think in terms of speed and modernity, rather, the principal focus should be on system security and system reliability in the context of delivering health services.

On the other hand, it is not meant to imply that nothing should be done until all legal questions are answered and all mechanical and technical problems are identified and solved. It is likely that we will not see some of the problems in proper focus until we actually attempt to institute changes in existing systems.

What then are the ways in which sensible changes can be brought about? Change may come through administrative action, through legislative action, possibly through judicial action and by means of cooperative action of private organizations and associations. Let us examine the feasibility of these approaches by first reviewing the functions (and limitations) of each branch of government.

Section 1
Administrative Action

Administrative agencies, which are the prime source for regulation of medical records, are found in the executive branch of government. Officials in this branch are charged with the duty of executing the law, formulating and applying policy and maintaining the day-to-day operations of government. Licensing and regulatory boards have the power to make regulations and to enforce them even to the extent of suspending or revoking licenses previously granted. They can deny applications for initial licensure. They can inspect licensed individuals and institutions and they can decide controversies.

In theory, the legislature enacts the law, the executive branch enforces the law and the judicial branch interprets the law and decides controversies. In practice, however, administrative agencies may perform all three of these functions because legislation grants them the power to issue regulations, enforce them and punish violations. The administrative agencies which regulate medical records will be the primary focus of the thrust for change.

As noted in Chapter III, the California Department of Health has amended its hospital regulations and has interpreted the amended language so as to permit the application of data processing techniques to the maintenance of required records. Other state administrative agencies may be approached to amend or interpret their existing regulations. They may be asked to adopt new regulations. Yet the rule-making procedure can be complicated and drawn out. Rules may be formulated in a variety of ways:

1. Unilateral action of the agency.

2. Informal discussions with interested persons.

3. Creation of advisory committees which represent various interest groups.

4. Formal hearings followed by closed deliberations and the announcement of a ruling.

Some administrative agencies are required to follow a format which is detailed in a state administrative procedures act. These acts set forth rule-making procedures with regard to the participation of interested parties. Essentially each act requires that notice is published of intended administrative action indicating the terms and substance of the action, and the time, place and manner in which interested persons may present their views. These acts also require that all interested persons be given a reasonable opportunity to submit data, views and arguments.

However, a good deal of rule-making today is done without participation of interested parties. Informal, written or oral consultation with affected parties or with advisory committees is also an important part of the rule-making procedure. Often the effectiveness of a particular group in the rule making process depends upon specific knowledge of the key personnel of the agency. There are practical as well as procedural considerations which have to be taken into account in the rule-making process.

Interested persons do not have to wait for the agency to make the first move, they may initiate action. There is no guarantee that an agency will act favorably upon a request. Under some state administrative procedures acts, an interested party may request an agency to issue, amend or repeal a rule or regulation. Within a stated period of time—usually 30 days—after submission of the request, the agency must either deny the request in writing stating the reasons therefor or it must initiate rule-making proceedings which will dispose of the matter after formal hearings.

In some states the agency may be requested to render an advisory opinion on the applicability of a regulation to a specific fact situation. There are disadvantages to this approach. If the opinion is unfavorable it may preclude future change. If it is favorable there is no guarantee that it will lead to a modification of an existing regulation.

The attorney general—an officer in the executive branch of government—may be asked to render an opinion as to the legality of automated medical recordation techniques under existing regulations. Opinions of attorneys general are a minor but important source of law. In some states the opinions are available in published forms. The attorney general may be formally requested to render his opinion on a specific legal question involving, generally, a subject about which the law is unclear. If he does render an opinion, it will carry with it the prestige of his office and it may have persuasive weight in courts. This procedure has inherent deficiencies because the opinion does not have the authority of a statute or judicial decision. However, on other health matters attorneys general have been requested to render advisory opinions. In New York and Rhode Island, for example, the attorney general was officially requested and did render an opinion with reference to the administration of intravenous fluid by nurses.

Another disadvantage of opinions of attorneys general is that they will answer only the specific questions asked. If the question is very specific the answer, even if favorable, may not be generally applicable. Moreover, in many states the attorney general will render an opinion only at the formal request of an administrative agency.

Section 2
Legislative Action

The state legislature may be approached to enact legislation which would provide for the acceptability of electronic data processing systems in medical record keeping. The legislative branch has the authority to hold hearings through its committee structure to obtain information and views relating to the necessity and propriety of legislative action. After due consideration, legislation may be drafted. Again, after deliberation, the proposed legislation—called a "bill"—may be voted on. If both houses of the legislature agree by affirmative vote, the proposed legislation is sent to the governor for signature.

The governor can allow the bill to become law without his signature, sign it into law or veto the legislation. If the legislation is vetoed, the legislature can override the governor's veto in some cases.

The process a bill may undergo varies from state to state, but generally the legislative process will include:

Hearings to determine the need for legislation.

Writing proposed legislation.

Introduction of proposed legislation into the legislative process.

Submission to a committee for evaluation and revision.

Report by committee.

Discussion and debate.

Amendment or modification of proposed legislation.

Vote on proposed legislation.

Submission to a joint committee of both houses to reconcile differences in language.

Enactment.

Submission to governor for his signature.

The legislative process is potentially a lengthy one and not at all conducive to rapid change. Assuming the legislature passed a new law, it could be merely a modification of the powers of the appropriate regulatory agency to allow it to issue regulations which would authorize the use of automation in medical recordation. Such a law would have to be specifically implemented by the agency. This would require many of the steps we have outlined in the discussion of administrative action. On the other hand, enactment would at least provide an indication of legislative interest which would assure some modification of the existing rule.

Section 3
Judicial Action

The courts may be requested to interpret a particular regulation in the light of modern technology. It is possible for an organization to apply to an appellate court to participate as a "friend of the court" in a case involving the specific regulation. Such cases seldom if ever appear. It may be possible to request a court to render a declaratory judgment which literally is an interpretation of how the law would affect certain activity. The procedures and standards for obtaining a declaratory judgment vary markedly from state to state. Finally, it is conceivable that one might develop a test case to bring about judicial review of an existing regulation. However, the likelihood of success in the judicial approach is extremely remote.

Section 4
Private Action

The relevant private organizations in the state may jointly develop guidelines and procedures for the application of automation to medical records. This approach has been taken by health organizations with reference to the disclosure of information from medical records.

Organizations in several states have attempted to solve scope of nursing practice problems by joining together to write and sponsor joint statements which set forth reasonable and carefully considered rules. In Pennsylvania, for example, the Medical Society, the Hospital Association, Osteopathic Association, the League for Nursing and the Nurses' Association all joined to write and sponsor a statement which recognized that licensed professional nurses could administer fluids intravenously with proper training and on the order of a physician.

While a statement of this nature does not have the force of law, it may serve as a guide to administrative agencies and it indicates that recognized health organizations, after careful and serious considerations took a written position on a matter of common concern.

It should be clear that bringing about change, even through the administrative process, is difficult at best. The organizations interested in change

117

should first meet to define the problems involved and to develop methods by which those problems can be solved. A justification will have to be established which supports the need for change.

As has been said repeatedly system security and system reliability will remain constant requirements in any alternative system. There is some question as to whether or not the present method of medical recordation actually provides system security and system reliability. It may be that the present form and condition of medical records are important reasons for bringing about automation. The methods of collection and recording the data are so variable and so disparate that the entire system of recordation may have to be overhauled. Indeed, variations exist not only from hospital to hospital but within the hospital itself.

It is therefore necessary to look at the present system most carefully to identify its defects and to build methods of correcting these defects so that the medical record indeed becomes an effective means of communication among those who provide health care. The capabilities of the computer, even at the present day, are so significant that it is important that only meaningful, comprehensible information is placed in its storage or memory.

While present rules and regulations governing hospital medical records generally require the signature of the attending physician and while nurses may also be required to initial their notes and observations, few if any regulations set forth a standard method or system of writing the orders or notes. As the cases we have discussed in the chapter on liabilities indicate, a wide variety of misleading orders and observations are placed in the records. The fact that a record is signed does not give the information reliability. It merely tells us which physician or nurse wrote a confusing order or note.

The point is that there are vital changes to be made before the movement to automation can be made, and these changes can be developed without governmental intervention. If we are to use computers to aid in medical recordation and evaluation, if we are to take advantage of automation for medical diagnosis, analysis of laboratory tests and research, we had better be precisely certain that all parties to the endeavor speak the same language and communicate in the same mode. The requirement of clarity, explicitness and uniformity far exceeds our present practices, and perhaps capability.

This means at the least that the schools of medicine, nursing and the health professions, the institutions which train medical record librarians and technicians, the institutions which provide in-service training and the professional organizations must develop a standard language. The task is formidable but not impossible.

Moreover, accuracy and uniformity are not the only constraints upon the system. The information must be timely. It must be capable of retrieval within strict time limits so that those who must execute orders are able to perform their functions. Methods of input must be developed to permit rapid placement of information while at the same time providing for verification. It will still be necessary to require authentication and system security.

It is beyond the scope of this book to examine the problems involved in automated medical diagnosis. Suffice it to say that there are significant questions about the possibility of quantifying all aspects of the "art and science" of medicine. We must also face the question of whether we desire to build systems which may eventually replace humans who are very special in our scheme of things. There are hard judgments involved but we must be prepared to make them not only in engineering terms but in human terms as well.

Bringing about change, then involves much more than inducing an administrative agency to modify its regulations. There must be an awareness of all of the implications of computerization of the medical process. This awareness and the judgments which follow are prerequisites to the formulation of required change.

Leadership and the initiative for change will remain in the hands of the medical record librarians, physicians, nurses, and the computer industry.

STATE-BY-STATE ANALYSIS

This comprehensive compilation and analysis of state statutes and regulations affecting the application of automation to medical records will cite and quote significant language of legal materials deemed relevant. It will be found that there is a high degree of similarity among the states, yet each state has its own particular peculiarities. Language applicable to records in uniform acts, such as the Uniform Narcotic Drug Act and the Interstate Compact on Mental Health, will not be reported upon because the provisions are the same from state to state.

The statutes and regulations will be analyzed in terms of the following categories:

a. Creation and contents

b. Retention

c. Signature requirements

d. Disclosure authorized

e. Confidentiality

f. Other matters

a. *Creation and Contents:* This category will identify those statutes and regulations which make specific reference to the contents of the medical record and to the form it should take. Primary emphasis will be on those legal materials which appear by their very language to inhibit the easy transformation from a manual system to an automated one.

b. *Retention:* Here we shall deal with requirements which specify the manner in which and the length of time the record must be kept. Provisions relating to completion of records will be found here also. These materials vary significantly from state to state.

c. *Signature Requirements:* By far the greatest barrier to the creation of a truly automated system for medical records is the requirement that physicians and others must sign the record. The states vary in specificity, but the intent of a great majority of regulations and a number of statutes require that the physician sign or authenticate specified portions of the record as well as the record as a whole.

d. *Authorized Disclosures:* In this category we have placed those legal materials which specifically permit the disclosure of information from the record. Recently legislatures throughout the country have adopted a more liberal attitude toward disclosure—especially with reference to in-house evaluation and review procedures.

e. *Confidentiality:* This category will analyze those statutes and regulations specifically declaring that records or certain portions of information they contain are confidential. Statutes primarily deal with the physician-patient privilege which relates to court room testimony. The regulations are more general and appear to cover all situations.

f. *Other Matters:* This general category will report on statutes which deal with a variety of subjects such as admissibility, ownership and hospital lien laws.

If one or more of these items do not appear in the State-by-State Analysis, it means that nothing of significance was found in the statutes or regulations.

Alabama

a. *Creation and Contents:* The *Rules, Regulations and Standards for General and Special Hospitals,* Department of Public Health (January, 1967) contain many references to the contents and form of the record. The required contents of medical records are itemized at sections 703.1 through 703.6:

§703.1 *Admission Record.* This section provides that an "adequate permanent record either typewritten or legibly written with pen and ink shall be kept for each patient."

§703.2 *Medical and Surgical Record.* Minimum requirements are set out in the section. In addition to general information, the clinical section must include, when applicable, provisional diagnosis, laboratory and X-ray reports, consultations, medical and surgical treatment, operative report, tissue report, progress notes, final diagnosis, discharge summary (cases over 48 hours), and autopsy findings.

§703.3 *Obstetrical Record.* Prenatal, labor, and postpartum records must be maintained.

§703.4 *Newborn Record.* Birth record, physical examination, and nurse's record are required.

§703.5 *Physicians' Orders.* A specific record form for each patient is required for all physicians' orders.

§703.6 *Nurses' Record.* Personal services and observations shall be noted.

With reference to physical medicine, sections 1401.3 and 1401.4 require written records for all orders, treatments and procedures. Such records become a part of in-patients' medical records.

Certain notations to be made on the records of furloughed patients at mental hospitals are required by statute. Code of Ala. tit. 45 §219 (Recomp. 1958).

b. *Retention:* Section 701.1 of the health regulations places primary responsibility for maintenance of records on the administrator. Section 701.2 requires that records must be stored to assure safety from water or fire damage and unauthorized use. Section 701.3 provides that records shall be kept current. They must be stored for 22 years as either original records, abstracts, microfilm or otherwise. Nurses' notes may be deleted from the permanent record.

c. *Signature Requirements:* Numerous sections require signatures. Section 701.7 requires that entries in the medical record be made in ink or typewritten; they must be authenticated and signed or initialed by the attending physician. Section 703.5 is to the same effect, requiring the signature or initials of the attending physician for all orders. Verbal or telephonic orders must later be signed or initialed by the attending physician. Laboratory reports must be signed or initialed by the individuals performing the tests under section 901.5. Mechanical restraints, according to section 1201.2, can be applied only when the attending physician deems them necessary. The restraint orders must be in writing and signed by the attending physician within 24 hours. Section 1201.3 permits seclusion of patients only on written orders of the attending physician.

d. *Disclosure Authorized:* No statute or regulation specifically authorizes the disclosure of information from medical records. Section 502.1(4) requires that the medical staff bylaws provide for a monthly review and analysis of the medical staff's clinical experience using the patients' medical record as the basis for such review. However, section 701.8 provides that the hospital governing board shall determine the persons who shall have access to medical records. The State Mental Health Board has the power to set standards for the transfer of patients and their records. Code of Ala. tit. 22, §320(11) (Supp. 1969). The board of trustees of hospitals for the insane have the right of access to the wards and books and records of such hospitals at any time. Code of Ala. tit. 45 §203 (Recomp. 1958).

e. *Confidentiality:* There is no physician-patient privilege in Alabama. Section 701.8 of the health regulations specifically makes the contents of records confidential. Section 701.2 requires that the records be handled in such a manner as to assure that they are safeguarded from unauthorized use.

f. *Other Matters:* Several statutes refer to the admissibility of records or copies in judicial proceedings. When the original would be admissible in any suit or proceeding, a certified copy of the hospital record will be admissible in its place. The record may include admission, disease, injury, history, temperature and other charts, X-rays, written orders, directions, findings and reports and interpretations of "physicians, doctors, surgeons, pathologists, radiologists, specialists, dentists, technicians and nurses as well as of employees of such hospitals, forming part of such hospital records as to the health, condition, state, injuries, sickness, disease, mental, physical and nervous disorders, duration and character of disabilities, diagnosis, prognosis, progress, wounds, cuts, contusions, lacerations, breaks, loss of blood, incisions, operations, injuries, medication, medicines, supplies, treatment and care and the cost, expenses, fees and charges..." This information is admissible without further proof as business records of the hospital. Code of Ala. tit. 7, §383(1) (Supp. 1969).

On the question of ownership, section 701.4 of the Regulations provides that the records are the property of the hospital and cannot be removed except by court order. Control of the record rests with the hospital administrator.

Alaska

a. *Creation and Contents:* The *Regulations for the Licensing, Maintenance and Operation of Hospitals and Nursing Homes,* Department of

Health and Welfare (1961) contain many references to the contents and form of the medical record. These regulations are contained in one extensive section of the Alaska Administrative Code. Alas. Adm. Code tit. 7, §180.

Section 180(f) sets out the requirements for medical records. All patients shall have "accurate and complete confidential medical records." Minimum requirements for completeness include, where applicable, adequate identification data, admitting diagnosis, history and physical examination, progress notes, signed doctor's orders, operative notes, laboratory and X-ray reports, nurse's notes, discharge diagnosis, and autopsy report. Newborn infants will each have a medical record including a physical examination performed and recorded by the physician and a statement of physical condition at the time of discharge.

b. *Retention:* Section 180(f) (H) provides "All original hospital records or photographs of same shall be stored in the hospital, and none shall be disposed of except by the approval of the Department of Health and Welfare." This is the only reference found related to retention. The medical staff is required to have a policy for completion of medical records within a reasonable time. Completion is the responsibility of the attending physician.

c. *Signature Requirements:* Not only must all orders be signed by a member of the medical staff, but §180(f) (G) provides that "all medical records shall contain the orders for medication and other services written in ink and signed by the prescribing physician or countersigned by him within twenty-four (24) hours." Narcotic records must be signed or initialed. Psychiatric services must be authenticated by signed doctor's orders.

Alas. Stat. tit. 47 §47.30.140 (1962) dealing with the use of mechanical restraints in mental hospitals, provides that their use and reasons therefor shall be made part of the patient's clinical record over the signature of the head of the hospital, or his designee. Surgical cases must be signed by the attending physician and the doctor's written orders that indicate the need for restraints for psychiatric patients should be signed by the physician. After the patient has been admitted and the need arises the doctor should order restraints and if such order is by telephone he must sign it within 24 hours. In fact, all orders with reference to psychiatric patients have to be written in the record by the physician, except telephone orders.

d. *Disclosure Authorized:* The regulations provide that medical and nursing staffs shall have access to medical records. The hospital is responsible for the completeness and accuracy of the data furnished from its records.

e. *Confidentiality:* The Alaska privileged communications statute found at Alas. *Rules of Civil Procedure* Rule 43(h) (Supp. Sept. 1966) applies to physicians and surgeons and covers civil and criminal actions. Any information acquired in attending the patient which was necessary to enable the physician to prescribe and act for the patient falls within the privilege. As indicated the regulation provides that "accurate and complete confidential medical records" are to be prepared for each patient.

Arizona

a. *Creation and Contents:* The *Rules and Regulations for the Licensing of Hospitals,* State Department of Health (June, 1964) contain only the following language concerning medical records:

> Sec. 4-2-4.1 CLINICAL RECORDS
>
> An accurate and complete physical examination and medical history shall be made of and recorded within 24 hours of admission for each patient admitted to the hospital. These records shall be kept up to date and filed in an accessible manner with provisions for their safe storage in the hospital.

e. *Confidentiality:* The privileged communication statute found at Ariz. Rev. Stat. §12-2235 (1956) applies to civil and criminal actions and covers communications made by the patient with reference to any physical or supposed physical disease or any knowledge obtained by personal examination of the patient. This language is restated at Ariz. Rev. Stat. §13-1802 (1956).

f. *Other Matters:* The hospital lien law found at Ariz. Rev. Stats. §§33-932 to -935 (1956), does not specifically require the institution to furnish copies of records.

Pursuant to Ariz. Stat. §36-151 (Supp. 1970), a home health agency is one which, among other things, "maintains clinical records on all patients."

Arkansas

a. *Creation and Contents:* The *Rules and Regulations for Hospitals and Related Institutions in Arkansas,* Department of Health, PART SIX (1969) provide complete references to the form and contents of medical records.

Record contents shall include complete identification data, family history, chief complaints, physical examination, orders and progress notes (dated and signed), provisional and final diagnosis, and discharge summary. When applicable the record shall include laboratory and X-ray reports, consultation reports, complete surgical records, obstetrical records (prenatal, labor, postpartum), newborn records, physical therapy, autopsy findings, and nurse's notes.

The original or a copy of the original of all reports must be included in the medical record. The regulations provide that the record shall be permanent and either typewritten or legibly written in ink.

b. *Retention:* Patient records must be completed within 15 days of discharge. The regulations require that index cards and "a recognized system for the indexing of records by disease, operation, and physician shall be maintained and kept up-to-date." Patients' records must be kept in a fire resistant place.

With regard to preservation, the regulation states that "Records and reports of findings shall be kept either in the original or by microfilm for ten (10) years after known death or 99 years."

c. *Signature Requirements:* Included among the numerous provisions which require signatures are orders and progress notes (verbal orders must be signed within 24 hours), date and time of death, laboratory reports, X-ray reports, therapy reports, pathological reports, anesthetic reports, operative reports, and, of course, the various consent authorizations.

The regulations provide that a rubber stamp signature of a physician shall be acceptable "only if a valid reason exists as to why the physician cannot sign the document in his own handwriting." Where such reason exists only the physician can possess and use the stamp, and a statement to that effect must be on file in the administrative office of the hospital.

d. *Disclosure Authorized:* Only personnel authorized by the administrator may have access to medical records. However, the records are to be made available to Health Department personnel.

e. *Confidentiality:* The medical records are considered confidential material, but written consent of the patient or his legal guardian shall be presented as authority for the release of information. Medical records are expressly excluded from the "Freedom of Information Act." Ark. Stat. Ann. §12-2804 (Repl. 1968)

f. *Other Matters:* Medical records shall not be removed from the "hospital environment" except on subpoena by a court having legal authority, to issue such an order. The privilege communication statute, Ark. Stat. Ann. §28-607 (Repl. 1962), applies to physicians and surgeons and trained nurses. It is also made applicable to criminal matters by §43-2004 (Repl. 1964). A separate statute, §72-1516 (Repl. 1957), applies to psychologists.

The scope of the statute is limited. It covers any information acquired in attending the patient which was necessary to enable the doctor to prescribe or act for the patient except that in cases involving wills, real estate and conveyances, the physician may testify as to the patient's mental capacity. Other exceptions cover actions against a physician where the patient is deemed to consent to testimony by the attending physician; the survivors of a deceased patient may consent to disclosure and an action for the death of the patient is deemed a consent to disclosure.

California

a. *Creation and Contents:* The regulations of the State Department of Health (May, 1968, as amended), require that records be kept on all patients admitted. All records are to be kept as originals or as "faithful and accurate reproductions of the contents of such originals." Cal. Adm. Code tit. 17, §280 (as amended 1969) This language has been interpreted to permit the application of electronic data processing techniques to the maintenance of required records.

The regulations specify the contents of admission records as well as medical records, which must contain among other things, diet orders, progress notes by physician and nurses' notes. Nurses' notes must include a record of the type of restraint and the time of application and removal as well as a record of pertinent observations including psychosocial manifestations.

b. *Retention:* The record must be safely preserved for seven years following the discharge of the patient, except that records of minors must be kept at least one year after the minor has reached the age of 21, and in any event not less than seven years.

If a facility ceases to operate, the Health Department must be notified of the arrangements made for safe preservation of the patients' records. Upon a change in ownership both the previous licensee and the new licensee shall have custody of the patient's records, that the records are to be available to both the old and new licensee and the regulations also provide that arrangements have been made for the safe preservation of the records.

c. *Signature Requirements:* Pursuant to section 287, no medication or treatment shall be given except on the signed order "of one lawfully authorized to give such an order," except in emergencies when the physician may give an order by telephone. The physician must sign the order within 48 hours. Section 355 requires a physician's signed order for the use of restraints. In cases of clear-cut emergency a telephone order may be given but the physician must sign it on his next visit.

d. *Disclosure Authorized:* Records are required to be legible and readily available upon the request of the attending physician, the hospital, its medical staff or any authorized officer, agent or employee of either as well as "any other person authorized by law to make such a request."

e. *Confidentiality:* The California privileged communication statute applies to licensed physicians or surgeons pursuant to Cal. Evid. Code §§990-1007 (1968). It covers civil actions and applies to any information acquired when a patient consults a physician to obtain a diagnosis or submits to an examination. Section 998 expressly excludes the privilege in criminal proceedings. Other exceptions specified in the code are: (1) actions where a patient-plaintiff offers his condition as an issue, (2) where services of a physician were sought to commit or plan a crime or a tort, (3) proving the validity of wills, real estate conveyances, and information relevant to an issue of breach of duty in a physician-patient relationship.

Colorado

a. *Creation and Contents:* The contents of hospital records are specified in considerable detail by the Colorado licensing standards. *Standards for Hospitals and Health Facilities,* Department of Public Health, §§4.1-4.9 (1965). The standards require that a complete medical record be maintained on every patient from the time of admission through discharge. Items to be included in the contents are sociological data, medical-surgical data and nurses' records. Medical-surgical data includes, personal and family history, physical examination reports, provisional diagnosis, clinical and pathological laboratory findings, X-ray reports, consultation reports, treatment and progress notes, complete surgical and dental reports (when applicable), final diagnosis, and autopsy protocol, if any.

The regulations for obstetric records provide an excellent example of the completeness required for medical records generally:

§4.7 CONTENT, OBSTETRIC. Records of all obstetric patients shall include, in addition to the requirements for medical records, the following:

Record of previous obstetric history and prenatal care including blood serology, and RH factor determination.

Admission obstetrical examination report describing conditions of mother and fetus.

Complete description of progress of labor and delivery, including reasons for induction and operative procedures.

Records of anesthesia, analgesia, and medications given in the course of labor and delivery.

Records of fetal heart rate and vital signs.

Signed report of consultants when such services have been obtained.

Names of assistants present during delivery.

Progress notes including descriptions of involution of uterus, type of lochia, condition of breast and nipples, and report of condition of infant following delivery.

b. *Retention:* Section 4.2 provides that the records shall be preserved permanently as original records or on microfilm. A completed medical record shall be retained in the medical record room following the patient's discharge. The regulation also provides that legal counsel should be obtained prior to disposition of medical records. Section 4.4 makes completion of the record the responsibility of the attending physician.

c. *Signature Requirements:* Numerous references to signatures are found in the regulations. Section 4.4 relating to entries states that all orders for diagnostic procedures, treatments and medications and all reports shall be entered into the medical record in ink or by typewriter. Such orders or reports are to be signed by the attending physician.

Section 3.6 relating to the medical staff requires that each record be authenticated and signed by a licensed physician; those for dental treatment must also be signed by a licensed dentist. Sections 3.7 and 4.7 require the signatures of consultants. The attending surgeon must write a complete description of operative procedures and findings including post-operative diagnosis and he must sign the record promptly following the operation. Reports of physical examination of newborns must be signed by the attending physician.

Section 19-26, requires that reports of medications administered shall be signed by persons administering them.

The written report of the findings and evaluations of each X-ray examination or treatment shall be signed by the physician responsible for the procedure.

d. *Disclosure Authorized:* Under section 3.6 the medical record committee of the medical staff is responsible for supervising and appraising the quality of medical records. Colo. Rev. Stat. §66-12-5 (Supp. 1967) requires pathological laboratories to report to the department of public health cases of tuberculosis. Section 66-12-8 (Supp. 1967) permits health department employees to inspect and have access to all medical records of all institutions and clinics where tuberculosis patients are treated. Under Colo. Rev. Stat. §71-1-7 (1963) dealing with commitment of mental defectives, the medical commission has the authority to examine hospital and medical records and reports.

e. *Confidentiality:* The privileged communications statute, found at Colo. Rev. Stat. §§154-1-7 to -8 (1963), applies to physicians and surgeons authorized to practice in any state and covers any information acquired in attending the patient which was necessary to enable him to prescribe or act for the patients. An exception to the act is made for malpractice suits brought by a patient or his heirs.

Another section makes this privilege applicable to criminal actions. Colo. Rev. Stat. §39-8-2 (1963) allows physicians to testify in criminal court actions where there is a plea of insanity, as to their conclusions reached after examination of hospital records, and other reports. The reports, however, have to be produced at the time of trial.

Connecticut

a. *Creation and Contents:* Section 19-13-D3(d) of the Public Health Code promulgated pursuant to Conn. Gen. Stat. §19-13 (Supp. 1967) requires that a medical record be started for each patient at the time of admission. The requirement includes admission notes and orders of the attending resident physician as well as general provisions concerning doctors' orders, nurses' notes and charts.

b. *Retention:* The records must be filed in an accessible manner in the hospital and shall be kept for a minimum of 25 years after discharge of the patient, except that the original medical records may be destroyed sooner if they are microfilmed by an approved process. Medical records must be completed within 14 days after discharge of the patient. Persistent failure by a physician to maintain proper records of his patients, promptly prepared and completed, are ground for suspension or withdrawal of medical staff privileges.

c. *Signature Requirements:* The regulation provides that all entries shall be signed by the person responsible for them.

d. *Disclosure Authorized:* Conn. Gen. Stat. §4-104 (1958) requires each public or private hospital, upon demand of a patient after discharge, to permit the patient, his physician or his attorney to examine his hospital record including history, bedside notes, charts, pictures, and plates. Copies may also be made.

Conn. Gen. Stat. §4-105 (1958) indicates the procedure which the patient may follow when his request to examine his records has been refused. The patient may obtain a court order which requires the officer authorized to act as manager of the hospital to bring the records, plates, notes and charts to a judge of the Superior Court so that the patient or his physician or attorney may copy them.

e. *Confidentiality:* State department of health records of studies about maternal and prenatal morbidity and mortality, whether conducted by the department or other organizations are confidential and will not be admissible in any court. Excepted from this section are accepted practices concerning disclosure of regular hospital and medical records.

f. *Other Matters:* Conn. Gen. Stat. §4-104 (1958) also provides for the admissibility into evidence of copies of hospital records if an affidavit accompanies the copy and certifies that the record was made in the regular course of business. This section further provides that the subpoena must be served not less than 24 hours before the time for production of the record.

Delaware

a. *Creation and Contents:* The *Rules and Regulations of the State Board of Health* (January, 1967) contains only one specific reference to medical records. It requires that written orders signed by a member of the medical staff shall be required for all medications and treatments given to patients.

d. *Disclosure Authorized:* Several statutes relating to payment for care of the indigent specify that the hospital should keep records of patients on forms required by the County Levy Court. Investigators may inspect the records. Del. Code Ann. tit. 19 §2322 (Supp. 1968) allows an employee making a claim for workmen's compensation to inspect, copy and reproduce any medical records pertaining to him. Medical records is defined to include hospital records.

f. *Other Matters:* The Hospital Line Law at Del. Code Ann. tit. 25, §§4301 to 4306 (1953) requires the hospital to make medical records pertaining to the injured person available to the party claimed to be liable for the injury.

District of Columbia

a. *Creation and Contents:* The medical record requirements are found in *District of Columbia Regulations* tit. 8, ch. 7 (as amended 1967). References to medical records are found throughout section 8-7:124. It provides that medical records shall conform to the requirements of the 1960 standards of the Joint Commission on Hospital Accreditation. It is to be noted that new standards were approved in 1969. The following language under section 8-7:108 "general requirements" permits the use of automation:

> (j) *Records.* Any record other than medical records, required to be maintained by these regulations shall be properly filed for a period of not less than three years. Records may be maintained on microfilm, in photostatic form in electronic data processing equipment, or in some other suitable state.

b. *Retention:* Some records, as indicated above, may be maintained in an automated form. The specific section dealing with retention of the medical record requires that it must be filed in a safe place for not less than 10 years after the patient's discharge, "either in the form of the original copy or in the form of a microfilm or photostatic copy." No mention is made of electronic data processing equipment. There appears to be some conflict between the language of section 8-7:108 and that of section 8-7:124. However, an amendment to section 8-7:124 would resolve doubt.

c. *Signature Requirements:* Medication orders must be signed by a physician or dentist.

e. *Confidentiality:* The privileged communication statute applies to physicians or surgeons and covers any information confidential in its nature which was acquired in attending the patient in a professional capacity and which was necessary to enable him to act in that capacity whether the information came from the patient, his family or from persons in charge of him. D.C. Code §14-307 (1967)

Florida

a. *Creation and Contents:* The *Rules of the State Board of Health,* Chapter 170 D-1, provide at §170 D-1.12(2), that all clinical information pertaining to a patient shall be centralized in the patient's record. The record is to contain identification data, complaint, present illness, past history, family history, physical examination consultations, clinical laboratory reports, X-ray reports, provisional diagnosis, tissue reports, treatment (medical and surgical), progress notes, formal diagnosis and autopsy findings.

Section 465.021, Fla. Stat. Ann. (1965), provides that medication orders are not prescriptions.

c. *Signature Requirements:* Staff physicians are responsible for authentication by signature.

d. *Disclosure Authorized:* The Donation Statute, Fla. Stat. Ann. §736.18 (1964), provides a form on which the donor may authorize a physician, surgeon, hospital or medical school to examine and copy his record.

e. *Confidentiality:* A patient-psychiatrist privilege is found at Fla. Stat. Ann. §90.242 (Supp. 1970). It specifically applies to records relating to diagnosis or treatment of the patient's mental condition.

Georgia

a. *Creation and Contents:* The *Rules and Regulations for Hospitals,* Department of Public Health (1969), contain comprehensive requirements for the contents of medical records at §270-3-2-.11.

Records must be kept on all patients. Sufficient information must be included so as to validate the diagnosis and provide a foundation on which the treatment is given. The normal contents should include, where applicable, admission and discharge date, admitting and final diagnosis, condition on discharge, attending physician's signature, history and physical examination, treatment, physician's orders, progress notes, nurse's notes, medication, special examinations and reports, consultation record, autopsy findings, and discharge summary.

The admitting diagnosis must be recorded within 24 hours after admission.

b. *Retention:* Medical records are to be preserved in original form or microfilms, or "other useable forms." Hospitals must retain all medical records at least until the sixth anniversary of the patient's discharge. In the case of a minor the record must be maintained until his twenty-seventh birthday.

c. *Signature Requirements:* The regulation requires that all orders for patients be signed by the physician. Telephonic orders must be signed within 48 hours by the doctor.

The regulation further requires:

(7) Practitioner's progress notes signed by the attending practitioner shall be written for all patients as often as the need of the patient indicates. Such notes shall be entered at least weekly.

In a mental hospital, mechanical restraints may be applied only after a written order, signed by the superintendent of a hospital (or his designee) is entered in the patient's chart. The record must indicate the justification for the use of restraints. Ga. Code Ann. §88-1615 (Rev. 1963).

e. *Confidentiality:* A Georgia statute provides an exception to the general right of inspection of public records. This exception includes medical records and similar files, "the disclosure of which would be an invasion of personal privacy." Ga. Code Ann. §40-2703 (Supp. 1969).

Hawaii

a. *Creation and Contents:* The *Public Health Regulations* Chapter 12, Board of Health (approved June, 1950) pertain to hospitals. The only reference to medical records requires adequate space for the processing and storage of medical records, currently active and inactive. Copies of legal process or papers served on a patient in a psychiatric facility must be filed with his records pursuant to Haw. Stat. §334.58 (1968).

d. *Disclosure Authorized:* The appeals committee of the Waimano Training School and Hospital is authorized to review a patient's clinical and psychological records, pursuant to Haw. Stat. §333-32 (1968).

The director of health may inspect records of patients in the state hospital pursuant to section 334-35 (1968).

The chief of police of Honolulu, any coroner and the coroner's physician may examine the record of any hospital pertaining to any patient in connection with criminal investigations. The hospital may require written authority for such investigations. Haw. Stat. §715-17 (1968).

Idaho

a. *Creation and Contents:* The *Rules, Regulations, and Minimum Standards for Hospitals in Idaho,* Dept. of Health (1963, as amended 1968) specify the required contents of the record. The following items, in addition to general information, must be included in the record of each patient: special examination reports, consultation reports, nursing notes, treatment notes, progress notes, complete surgical and dental record (when applicable), graphic charts, final diagnosis, condition on discharge and "signed permission for surgery, anesthesia, autopsy, and other procedures when necessary."

b. *Retention:* Records must be kept for a minimum of seven years. In the case of a minor the record must be kept for seven years after his twenty-first birthday. The regulation also requires that records be safely stored. "This shall be deemed to mean that medical records are handled in such manner as to assure reasonable safety from water or fire damage and are safeguarded from unauthorized use."

The regulation further provides that it is desirable that records be permanently preserved either as original records, abstracts, micro-films, "or other reproductions to afford a basis for a complete audit of professional services rendered..." An elaborate procedure is spelled out for destruction of records at the closing of a hospital.

Completion of the medical record is the responsibility of the attending physician.

c. *Signature Requirements:* Physicians are required to sign treatment notes and progress notes. The anesthetist or anesthesiologist must sign the anesthesia record including post-anesthetic condition.

The attending surgeon must record and sign the operative record including operative procedure, finding and post-operative diagnostic impressions. Signature requirements are found in other regulations dealing with obstetrics and newborns.

Signatures for the use of restraints are not only required in the regulations but also by Idaho Code §66-345 (Supp. 1967). Prescriptions for narcotics must be in writing and signed by the prescriber. Idaho Code §37-3008 (Supp. 1967).

d. *Disclosure Authorized:* With reference to hospitalization of the mentally ill, Idaho Code §66-348 (Supp. 1967) provides that records are confidential except that (a) the individual may consent to disclosure, (b) disclosure may be made to carry out the provisions of the act, (c) the court may direct and the section does not preclude disclosure "upon proper inquiry" to members of the patient's family, relatives or friends, abstracts, title insurance companies, lawyers, physicians, or authorized hospital personnel. The regulations provide that the previous records are to be made available for the use of the physician attending a readmission.

e. *Confidentiality:* The physician-patient privilege applies to civil and criminal matters and covers any information acquired in attending the patient which is necessary to enable the physician to prescribe or act for the patient. The patient can waive the privilege. There is also an exception for cases of suspected child abuse. Idaho Code §9-203 (Supp. 1967).

Illinois

a. *Creation and Contents:* The regulations set forth the minimum requirements for medical records:

> (b) For each patient there shall be adequate, accurate, and
> complete medical records. A minimum medical record shall

include the following data: identification; admission information; personal and family history; complaint; history of present illness; physical examination; special examinations, if any, such as consultations, laboratory and x-ray tests; provisional or working diagnosis; medical treatment; surgical record, if any; nurses' notes; progress notes; final diagnosis; condition on discharge; in case of death—autopsy findings, if any. *Hospital Licensing Act and Requirements,* Dept. of Public Health, PART XII (1968, as amended 1969).

b. *Retention:* Original records or photographs of such records are required to be preserved in accordance with the recommendations of the American Hospital Association and legal opinions. Provision is required for safe storage of the record including safety from fire or water damage and unauthorized use.

c. *Signature Requirements:* Laboratory reports must be signed "or otherwise authenticated." Signed reports of tissue examination are to be filed with the patient's record.

e. *Confidentiality:* The physician-patient privilege applies to any information the physician or surgeon may have acquired in attending the patient in a professional capacity which was necessary to enable him to treat the patient. It does not apply to homicide trials, mental illness inquiries, actions against a physician for malpractice, wills, criminal abortion trials and of course, where the patient consents. Ill. Stat. Ann. ch. 51, §5.1 (1966)

Indiana

a. *Creation and Contents:* Section 3.3b requires that a medical record, in writing, be maintained for each patient admitted. *Requirements for Licensure Under the General Regulations for Hospitals, Indiana, 1959,* Board of Health (Reprinted 1964).

Section 6.1j provides that the information contained should give a complete picture of the patient's needs and the care rendered. Requirements include: general information, progress notes, written reports of consultations, laboratory, x-ray, and operative reports, doctor's orders properly signed [See Signature Requirements], nurses' notes, temperature sheets, final discharge summary, final diagnosis, complications, and operative procedures signed by the attending physician on the face of the summary sheet.

b. *Retention:* Section 3.3b (HHL 9) provides in part as follows:

> Original medical records or photographs thereof shall be kept on file in a record in storage room and shall not be disposed of except on approval of the Hospital Licensing Council and the State Board of Health. In the event a hospital is to be

closed, its officers should inquire of the Council how to dispose of its registers and medical records. In determining whether an original record of a patient may be destroyed, due care must be given to meeting requirements of certain statutes of limitations.

* * *

(d) Generally the Hospital Licensing Council and the State Board of Health will not authorize the disposal of original hospital records that are less than 25 years old, unless preserved in the manner provided by [statute] and provided that the age and character of the record do not violate any of the statutes of limitations which are applicable. The original records themselves must be kept for at least five (5) years.

This section further provides that representatives of the medical staff shall work with the medical records librarian to ensure that the patient records are complete.

Iowa

a. *Creation and Contents:* The Iowa hospital regulations are in the process of revision. Those existing, *Rules and Regulations for Hospitals and Related Institutions,* Department of Health (1954), contain a general requirement for the maintenance of accurate and complete medical records.

b. *Retention:* Records are to be filed and stored in an accessible manner in the hospital in accordance with the statute of limitations.

c. *Signature Requirements:* The regulations provide that accurate and complete medical records shall be written for all patients and signed by the attending physician.

e. *Confidentiality:* The physician-patient privilege applies to any confidential communication entrusted to a physician in his professional capacity. Iowa Code Ann. §622.10 (Supp. 1970). It applies not only to the physician or surgeon but also to his stenographer or clerk who receives the information during the course of his employment. It covers criminal and civil proceedings.

f. *Other Matters:* While health research reports, records and data are confidential, the primary medical or hospital records are admissible into evidence.

Kansas

a. *Creation and Contents:* The *Kansas Hospital Regulations,* Board of Health (1969), list the required contents of medical records:

28-34-9 MEDICAL RECORD DEPARTMENT.

* * *

e. The medical record shall contain, when appropriate, identification data, chief complaint, present illness, past history, family history, physical examination, provisional diagnosis, clinical laboratory reports, physician's orders, radiological reports, consultations, medical and surgical treatment, tissue reports, progress notes, care given, pertinent observations, final diagnosis, hospital dismissal summary, and autopsy findings.

Regulation 28-34-9q specifically allows for automation of medical records: "Nothing in these regulations shall be construed to prohibit the use of properly automated medical records or use of other automated techniques, provided the regulations stated herein are met."

b. *Retention:* Medical records are to be maintained "in retrievable form" for twenty-two years after the date of the last discharge of the patient.

c. *Signature Requirements:* Each clinical entry must be signed or initialed by the attending physician who must be properly identified in the record. Nursing notes and observations must be signed by a registered nurse. Written reports of findings and evaluation of radiological examinations must be signed by the physician responsible and must be made a part of the patient's permanent record. Use of restraints must be authorized by the head of the hospital or a member of the medical staff along with a statement of the necessity for the use of such restraints. The statement must be signed and made a part of the patient's record, pursuant to Kan. Stat. Ann. §59-2928 (Supp. 1969).

e. *Confidentiality:* Pursuant to Kan. Stat. Ann. §59-2931 (Supp. 1969), records relating to the care and treatment of the mentally ill are confidential and shall not be disclosed except (a) on the consent of the patient, (b) on the sole consent of the head of the hospital if such disclosure is necessary for the care and treatment of the patient, (c) on order of any court, (d) in proceedings in the Probate Court. The physician-patient privilege applies to communications made by the patient with reference to any physical or supposed physical disease, ailment or injury. If no objection is raised, the physician may be required to testify. Kan. Stat. Ann. §60-427 (Supp. 1969).

Kentucky

a. *Creation and Contents:* The regulations for hospitals are found in a compilation of licensing laws and regulations for hospitals, nursing homes and convalescent homes. The Kentucky State Board of Health is currently revising the regulations.

The present regulation requires "adequate and complete" medical records for all patients admitted to the hospital. Minimum requirements include, identification data, history and physical examination, special examinations, provisional diagnosis, doctor's orders, progress notes, nurses' notes, complete surgical record, temperature chart, final diagnosis and condition on discharge.

b. *Retention:* Records are to be retained for a minimum of five years and for such additional times as deemed necessary by the board of governors.

c. *Signature Requirements:* The regulation contains many references to signatures. All notes are to be legibly written or typed and signed. Doctor's orders and progress notes are to be dated and signed by the physician. A complete surgical record must be signed by the operating surgeon, including anesthesia record, pre-operative diagnosis, operative procedure and findings, post-operative diagnosis and tissue diagnosis by a qualified pathologist on all specimens surgically removed.

The regulations further provide that it is the responsibility of each attending physician or dentist to complete and sign the medical record of each patient as soon as practical after discharge. In addition, the regulations state that orders for medication shall be written in ink and signed by the prescribing physician or dentist. Verbal orders are to be countersigned on the next visit.

d. *Disclosure Authorized:* The regulations specifically authorize the routing of records to physicians for consultation and the inspection of records by authorized representatives of the Board of Health.

In the case of involuntary hospitalization, hospitals in which patients were treated must send patient records to the receiving hospitals.

e. *Confidentiality:* The scope of the physician-patient privilege is governed by the attorney-client privilege. Ky. Rev. Stat. §213.200. It provides that no attorney shall testify concerning a communication made to him, in his professional capacity, by his client, or his advice thereon without the client's consent. Pursuant to Ky. Rev. Stat. §210.235 records of mental patients are confidential and cannot be disclosed; however several exceptions are listed including disclosure to the family or friends of a patient of information as to the mental patient's condition. Pursuant to Ky. Rev. Stat. § 222.195, records of alcoholic patients are confidential. Reference is made to section 210.235 concerning exceptions to the rule of confidentiality.

Louisiana

a. *Creation and Contents: Rules, Regulations and Minimum Standards Governing Hospitals,* State Department of Hospitals, ch. VIII (1962), contains specific requirements for the contents of medical records.

Section 3 requires that a complete record must be written for each patient. Sections 4-6 pertain to minimum contents. The medical record should include identifying and sociological data, medical history, physical examination, medical orders, progress notes, summary report of the patient's course, treatment records, diagnostic procedures and nurse's record.

The medical record should also include, where applicable, consultation notes, consent forms, operative record, anesthesia report, pathological reports and obstetrical records. Separate records for newborns are required.

b. *Retention:* No specific time limit for retention is given. The only requirement is that the record be "filed in an accessible manner in the hospital."

c. *Signature Requirements:* Medication orders must be written and signed by a member of the medical staff. Telephone orders for medication must be initialed by the prescribing physician within 24 hours from the time they were given.

Medical history, physical examination, medical orders, progress notes, summary report and record of all medical care must be written, dictated, or prepared by or under the supervision of the attending physician. The face sheet of the complete patient chart must be signed by the doctor.

d. *Disclosure Authorized:* Upon transfer of a patient to a mental institution all of the patient's records or a full abstract must be sent. La. Stat. Ann. tit. 28 §94 (1951). Another statute relating to public records, provides in general that patient records are exempt, except in the case of poisoning, accident, or negligence which results in injury, assault or any act of violence. The section further states that the governing body of any public institution shall make rules under which the charts, records, reports, documents or other memoranda may be exhibited or copied by or for persons legitimately interested in the disease, mental or physical, or in the condition of patients. La. Stat. Ann. tit. 44 §7 (Supp. 1970).

e. *Confidentiality:* The physician-patient privilege applies in criminal matters and covers information made to the physician as a physician by or on behalf of his patient as well as results of examinations, medical opinion or other information. There are exceptions for court-appointed physicians, and any physician may be cross-examined as to the correctness of a certificate signed by him. La. Stat. Ann. tit. 15, §476 (1967).

f. *Other Matters:* Certified copies of hospital records, signed by appropriate hospital officials may be received in evidence as prima facie proof of their contents. However, opposing parties may still subpoena and examine the persons who made the original record. La. Stat. Ann. tit. 13 §§3714, 3715 (1967).

Maine

a. *Creation and Contents:* The *Requirements for Hospital Licensing,* Department of Health and Welfare (1945, as amended 1946) contain a few general references to medical records. One portion calls for accurate and complete records to be kept for each patient from the time of admission to the time of discharge. They are to include the nursing care given. Another portion requires operative records to be kept. Pursuant to Me. Rev. Stat. tit. 32 §3108 (Supp. 1970) physical therapy aides are prohibited from making entries in patient's records. Limitations on the rights of mental patients are to be made part of their clinical records in accordance with Me. Rev. Stat. tit. 34 §2254 (Supp. 1970).

e. *Confidentiality:* Maine enacted a privileged communications statute in 1969. Me. Rev. Stat. tit. 32 §3153 (Supp. 1970). It applies to civil and criminal proceedings, and provides that a licensed physician cannot be required to testify with regard to any information he may have acquired in attending, examining or treating the patient, if the information was necessary to enable him to provide professional care. There are several exceptions. (1) The patient has the right to request or consent to the testimony. (2) The privilege does not apply when the physical or mental condition of the patient is at issue in the case. (3) A court may deem the disclosure necessary in the interest of justice. (4) The physician must comply with legal requirements for reporting and disclosure.

f. *Other Matters:* The hospital lien law found at Me. Rev. Stat. tit. 10, § 3412 (Supp. 1970) requires hospitals to make their records available in order to determine the reasonableness of charges. The statute prohibits disclosure of records which indicate the nature of the injury to the patient, the nature of his condition or the state of his recovery.

Maryland

a. *Creation and Contents:* Section 19 of the hospital regulations governs medical records. *43G01 - Standards and Regulations for Acute General Hospitals and Special Hospitals,* Department of Health (1959).

"Medical records shall be written or dictated only by physicians or interns." Records must be written in permanent ink (not pencil or ball-point pen).

The medical record must include identification data, admission and discharge dates, complaint, personal and family history, physical examination, provisional diagnosis, treatment, special examinations, all physicians' orders and findings, nursing notes, and progress notes. Complete surgical records are required, where applicable.

c. *Signature Requirements:* The regulations contain numerous signature requirements. Section 8 requires that all diet orders must be written, dated and signed by the physician or his representative. Section 9 requires that standing or telephoned orders for medications and drugs be signed or initialed by the doctor. The operating surgeon must sign a statement indicating that delay of surgery would be detrimental, to dispense with a complete examination in an emergency. Section 19 requires the signature of the attending physician on the patient's medical record. Use of restraints, section 13, can only be based on written orders signed by the physician.

e. *Confidentiality:* Several statutes make the records, reports, notes and other information assembled by in-hospital staff committees, among other medical groups, confidential. Such information is not to be disclosed.

f. *Other Matters:* The hospital lien law, Ann. Code of Md. art. 63 §49 (Repl. Vol. 1968), provides that persons against whom a claim for personal injuries is made shall be permitted to examine hospital records to ascertain changes with regard to the period of confinement and the itemization of departmental charges. Notice of such inspection must be mailed to the patient.

Massachusetts

a. *Creation and Contents: Licensure Rules and Regulations for Hospitals and Sanatoria in Massachusetts,* Dept. of Public Health (1950, as amended 1968), contains a comprehensive list of the contents of medical records. The record must include admission and discharge date, identification data, chief complaint, history of present illness, past history, physical examination, provisional diagnosis, reports of special examinations or procedures, complete surgical and dental record, progress notes, graphic bedside charts, final diagnosis, and condition on discharge.

Extensive requirements exist for all operative records, obstetrical records and records of newborn infants.

b. *Retention:* While the regulations do not prescribe a specific time during which records must be retained, Mass. Gen. Laws Ann. Ch. 111 §70 (Supp. 1970), requires licensed hospitals or clinics and those supported in whole or part by the Commonwealth to keep records and medical histories of the treatment of cases under their care. The section provides for the destruction of the original from which they were made. The section further provides that the records may be destroyed forty-five years after the discharge or final treatment of the patient.

c. *Signature Requirements:* The regulations contain many references to signatures. Orders for treatment and all reports must be signed by the physician. The completed medical record must be signed by the physician. The anesthetist must sign the anesthesia record. The attending surgeon must sign the record of operative procedures, findings and post-operative diagnosis. Obstetrical consultants must sign their reports. Reports of initial physical examinations of newborn infants must be signed by the attending physician.

d. *Disclosure Authorized:* The regulations provide that confidential information obtained from medical records shall be furnished only on the written authority of the patient, the executor of his estate or his attending physician. Moreover, all previous records shall be made available to the physician attending a readmission. The provisions of chapter 111 section 70 allows a patient or his attorney to inspect the patient's record. A copy must be furnished on request and the payment of a reasonable fee.

e. *Confidentiality:* Records pertaining to mental health are confidential. There is no physician-patient privilege in Massachusetts.

f. *Other Matters:* Several statutory sections provide for the admissibility of hospital and medical records. Defendants in personal injury actions are permitted to subpoena hospital records.

Michigan

a. *Creation and Contents:* The requirements for medical records appear in *Rules and Minimum Standards for Hospitals,* Mich. Dept. of Public Health (1960).

Section 8.1 requires "accurate and complete" medical records for each patient admitted. The regulations specify the contents:

8.2 Patients' records shall include the following:

8.21 Admission date.

8.22 Admitting diagnosis.

8.23 History and physical examination.

8.24 Physician's progress notes.

8.25 Operation and treatment notes and consultations.

8.26 The physician's orders.

8.27 Nurse's notes including temperature, pulse, respiration, conditions observed and medication given.

8.28 Record of discharge or death.

8.29 Final diagnosis.

8.3 Additional records of patients having surgery shall include the following:

8.31 Details of the pre-operative study and diagnosis.

8.32 The pre-operative medication.

8.33 The name of the surgeon and his assistants.

8.34 Repealed.

8.341 The method of anesthesia.

8.342 The amount of anesthetic when measurable.

8.343 The name of the anesthetist.

8.35 The post-operative diagnosis, including pathological findings.

8.4 The report of special examinations such as laboratory, x-ray and pathology shall be kept in the patient's record.

b. *Retention:* No specific time limit is indicated in the regulations, however, they do provide that medical records shall be preserved as original records, abstracts, microfilms or otherwise.

c. *Signature Requirements:* Section 7.13 provides that medication or treatment can only be given on the written order of a physician. Sections 7.14 and 7.15 provide that verbal orders for medication be entered in the record as such by the person receiving the order, "initialed by the physician's initials per the receiver's initials and countersigned by the physician at the time of the next visit."

e. *Confidentiality:* The physician-patient privilege applies to civil and criminal cases. The exceptions include actions for personal injuries or malpractice where the patient produces medical witnesses on his own behalf, and cases involving the probate of wills. Mich. Stat. Ann. §27A.2157 (1962).

Minnesota

a. *Creation and Contents:* The regulations of the State Board of Health contain a broad requirement that accurate and complete records be kept. *Regulations for the Construction, Equipment, Maintenance, Operation and Licensing of Hospitals,* Minn. State Bd. of Health, Reg. 4214 (1955). However, there is a footnote to the regulation that itemizes the contents of a complete medical record. It is presumed that the footnote is an integral part of the regulation.

To be considered complete, medical records should include adequate identification data, admitting diagnosis, history and physical examination, progress notes, signed doctors' orders, operative notes, special reports, nurses' notes and discharge diagnosis. Medical records are required to be maintained on all newborn infants.

b. *Retention:* The chief administrative officer of any public or private hospital, with the approval of the governing board, may destroy records that are more than 10 years old, provided the records shall first have been trans-

ferred and recorded on photographic film. Minn. Stat. Ann. §145.32 (1946).
c. *Signature Requirements:* Regulation 4209d provides, "no medication or treatment shall be given to a patient except on the written order of a member of the medical staff." Telephone orders must be reduced to writing immediately upon receipt and the staff member must sign the order within 24 hours.

Regulation 4214f requires the attending physician to sign and complete the history and physical examination record prior to any surgical procedure except in case of emergency.

In mental hospitals, each use of restraints and the reason therefore must be made part of the patient's record, along with the signature of the head of the hospital or a member of the medical staff. Minn. Stat. Ann. §253A.17 (Supp. 1970).

e. *Confidentiality:* The physician-patient privilege applies in civil and criminal cases. It covers any information or opinion acquired in attending the patient which was necessary to enable the physician to treat the patient. In actions to recover benefits under certain insurance contracts, the beneficiaries are deemed to be the personal representatives of the deceased. The patient may consent to disclosure. Minn. Stat. Ann. §595.02 (1947).

f. *Other Matters:* Photographic or photostatic copies when certified by the custodian of the records, are admissible in evidence.

Mississippi

a. *Creation and Contents: Minimum Standards of Operation for Mississippi Hospitals,* Commission on Hospital Care (1962), chapter 24, contains the specific requirements for medical records.

The minimum requirements for medical records include adequate identification data, family, personal, past and present history of illness, consent forms, physical examinations, reports of special examinations, records of consultations, anesthesia and surgical reports, physicians' orders and progress notes, nurses' notes, charts and provisional and final diagnosis.

All medication and treatment orders must be written in ink.
b. *Retention:* Miss. Code 1942 §§7146-51 to -61 (Supp. 1968) provides minimum standards for preparing, maintaining and retiring hospital records. It is a comprehensive statute. Section 7146-54, relating to retention provides:

> Hospital records shall be retained, preserved and properly stored by the various hospitals for such periods of reasonable duration as may be prescribed in rules and regulations adopted by the licensing agency. Such rules and regulations may provide for different periods of such retention for the various constituent parts of any hospital records and may re-

quire that an abstract be made of pertinent data from any hospital records that may be retired as provided herein. Such rules and regulations may also provide for different periods of such retention for the various injuries, diseases, infirmities or conditions primarily causing or associated with the hospitalization. Provided, however, complete hospital records shall be retained for a period after discharge of the patient of at least (a) seven years in cases of patients discharged at death, except as may be otherwise hereinafter provided; (b) ten years in case of adult patients of sound mind at the time of discharge, except as may be otherwise hereinafter provided; (c) for the period of minority or other known disability of the patient plus seven additional years, but not to exceed twenty-eight years, in cases of patients under disability of minority or otherwise; or (d) for the period of minority or other known disability of any survivors hereinafter mentioned plus seven additional years, but not to exceed twenty-eight years, in all cases where the patient was discharged at death, or is known by the hospital to have died within thirty days after discharge, and the hospital knows or has reason to believe that such patient or former patient left one or more survivors under disability of minority or otherwise who are or are claimed to be entitled to damages for wrongful death of the patient under section 1453, Mississippi Code of 1942, Recompiled, or laws amendatory thereof. Upon the expiration of the applicable period of retention, any hospital may retire the hospital record.

The regulations require that hospitals must have a magnifying reader for examination of the record. The regulation also makes reference to the time periods quoted above and requires that medical records whether or not microfilmed must be retained for those periods.

c. *Signature Requirements:* Regulation 1404.2 requires all orders for medication and treatment to be signed by the prescribing physician. Verbal orders must be undersigned by the physician upon his next visit to the hospital. Regulation 2404 requires all notes in the medical record to be legibly written or typed and signed.

Regulation 2403 provides that completion of the medical record is the responsibility of the attending physician. The physician's signature is required to be on the completed record. This regulation further provides that staff regulations at the hospital must provide for suspension or termination of staff privileges where a physician is persistently delinquent in completing records.

d. *Disclosure Authorized:* The statute setting forth minimum standards provides that the records are the property of the hospital subject to reasonable access to the information it contains where good cause is shown by the patient, his personal representatives, or heirs, his attending medical personnel and his duly authorized nominees. Miss. Code 1942 §§7146-53. Miss. Code 1942 §1697 (Recomp. 1956) contains a privilege provision.

e. *Confidentiality:* The privileged communication statute is very broad. It applies to any legal proceeding and covers all communications made to a physician or surgeon by a patient under his charge or seeking his advice. Nothing in the minimum standards statute can impair the "privilege of confidence conferred by law on patients." Another statute gives any person who has the power or authority to consent to a medical or surgical procedure, the right to waive the physician-patient privilege for himself or other persons and consent to the disclosure of medical information, and the making and delivering of copies of medical records. The waiver of consent survives the death of the person who made or gave it. Miss. Code 1942 §7129-85.

Missouri

a. *Creation and Contents: Missouri Hospital Licensing Law, Regulations and Codes,* Division of Health (1960 revised, with 1962 amendments), contains specific requirements for the contents of records.

The regulations will be deemed to have been satisfied if the patients' records include identification data, present illness, past history, family history, history of present complaint, physical examination, special reports, provisional diagnosis, physicians' or dentists' orders, nurses' notes, final diagnosis, condition on discharge, necropsy and tissue reports, and certification as to accuracy and completeness by the attending physician or dentist. All records must be legibly prepared in ink or typewritten.

b. *Retention:* The regulations provide that medical records are to be retained for at least the minimum period established by statutes of limitations.

All physicians or dentists and employees must be "prompt" in completing medical records. The administrator is responsible for the completeness of the records.

c. *Signature Requirements:* All orders are to be signed or initialed and dated by the attending physician, dentist or chiropodist as soon as possible after the order. Drugs, treatment or appliances are not to be administered unless ordered by a physician, dentist or chiropodist, and such orders are in writing and signed.

d. *Disclosure Authorized:* Records or excerpts cannot be released from the record room except on the written order of the patient or by legal process. Records may be removed from the record room on the order of the administrator for purposes of research and study by qualified persons. It is desirable, but not mandatory that the attending physician, dentist or chiropodist also authorize disclosure of information from the record.

e. *Confidentiality:* The physician-patient privilege applies to information acquired in the professional relationship.

Montana

a. *Creation and Contents: Montana Licensing Law and Standards for Hospitals and Related Institutions,* State Board of Health (1966), contains the requirements for medical records at PART IX:

Section A *Patient Records*

1. *Admission and Clinical Records* - For each patient admitted there shall be adequate, accurate and complete medical records, either typewritten or legibly written in pen and ink. A minimum medical record shall include the following data: name; address; age; sex; marital status; date of admission; name and address of closest relatives, or person, or agency responsible for patient; name, address and telephone number of attending physician; admission diagnosis; history and physical examination; medication and treatment orders; nursing notes; progress notes; laboratory and X-ray reports; diagnosis and condition of patient at time of discharge and date of discharge; in case of death, autopsy findings, if any.

A complete surgical record shall be kept including consultations, anesthetic record, pre-operative diagnosis, operative procedure and findings, post-operative diagnosis, and tissue diagnosis on all specimens surgically removed.

A complete obstetrical record shall be kept of maternity patients including prenatal record (if available), labor record, delivery record and complete and separate newborn record similar to those of the American Academy of Pediatrics.

* * *

b. *Retention:* Original records or photographs of such records no longer in use are to be stored in the hospital. All records are to be maintained for twenty-five years after the date of last discharge of the patient. However, nurses' notes are to be kept for five years or until the patient is twenty-six years old, whichever is longer. When death occurs, records must be kept for five years after the date of proof of death. Prior to destroying a record a summary card must be prepared which must be a permanent record of the hospital.

c. *Signature Requirements:* No medication or treatment may be given except on the written and signed order of a person authorized to give such order in the state.

e. *Confidentiality:* The physician-patient privilege applies to civil and criminal proceedings and covers any information acquired in attending the patient.

Nebraska

a. *Creation and Contents: Regulations and Standards for Hospitals and Maternity Homes,* Department of Health (1958), provides a general description of medical record contents.

Records must be "adequate and complete." Items to be included are the admission date, physical examination, diagnosis, treatment and medication, prognosis, and nursing care. A record must be kept for each newborn infant.

b. *Retention:* Medical records must be preserved for not less than twenty-five years. If a hospital ceases operation professional records are to be disposed of in a manner approved by the Department.

c. *Signature Requirements:* The regulations provide:

> All physicians orders shall be written in ink or indelible pencil. Such orders shall be signed by the physician in charge and preserved on the patient's chart or in the established records of the institution.

d. *Disclosure Authorized:* Neb. Stat. §25-12-120, (Supp. 1967) provides an implied consent to the examination and inspection of medical records by hospital medical staff committees or utilization review committees for the purpose of studying and evaluating the necessity and quality of care provided. Immunity from suit is provided. Neb. Rev. Stat. §25-12, 121 (Supp. 1967).

e. *Confidentiality:* The physician-patient privilege applies to any confidential communication entrusted to a physician or surgeon in his professional capacity. Neb. Rev. Stat. §25-1206 (Reissue 1964) Exceptions include the introduction of evidence referring to a patient's physical or mental condition, either by the patient or his personal representative in the case of death. Neb. Rev. Stat. §25-1207 (Supp. 1967).

147

Nevada

a. *Creation and Contents: Operational Rules and Regulations for Health Facilities,* State Board of Health, Section V1 (1969), contains the medical records provisions. Medical records must contain "sufficient information to justify the diagnosis, warrant treatment and vindicate the end results."

The record must be either printed, typewritten or legibly written. Records must include, where applicable, identification data, admissions diagnosis, progress notes by the physician, chief complaint, consultations, nurse's notes, medication and treatment orders, diet orders, history and physical examination, laboratory reports, complete surgical record, complete obstetrical record and condition and diagnosis of patient when discharged.

b. *Retention:* Medical histories must be retained for twenty-five years; they may be microfilmed after ten years if stored on rolls. If unitized jackets or cards are used they may be microfilmed at the time of discharge. Current records must be completed within twenty-four hours, and records of discharged patients must be completed within fifteen days following discharge.

c. *Signature Requirements:* Records must be authenticated and signed by a licensed physician. Medication orders must be in writing and signed by the attending physician. In an emergency a verbal order may be given to a licensed nurse who must write it down and sign it. The physician must countersign the order within 72 hours. The regulation relating to pharmacy also contains the following language:

> Each medication shall be properly recorded in the patient's medical record and signed by the individual responsible.

Laboratory reports must be signed and filed with the patient's record. Tissue reports must be signed by the pathologist. X-ray reports must be signed by the radiologist and filed with the patient's record.

e. *Confidentiality:* The physician-patient privilege applies to civil and criminal matters and covers any information acquired in attending the patient. Exceptions to the protection are malpractice actions, probate of wills, wrongful death actions, actions for personal injuries and actions involving insurance. Nev. Rev. Stat. §48.080 (1970). The superintendent of a mental hospital may restrict disclosure of information in medical records by establishing and enforcing reasonable rules governing their custody, use and preservation. Nev. Rev. Stat. §433.123 (1970).

f. *Other Matters:* The lien law permits anyone against whom a claim is asserted for damages for injuries to examine and copy all records related to the injured person. Nev. Rev. Stat. §108.640 (1970).

New Hampshire

a. *Creation and Contents: Rules, Regulations and Standards for the Operation of Hospitals,* Dept. of Health and Welfare (1969), contains the general requirements for the content of medical records.

The regulation provides:

4900 *Medical Records*

4910. There shall be accurate and complete records written for all patients and filed in an accessible manner in the hospital, a complete medical record being one which includes identification data; complaint; personal and family history; history of present illness; physical examination; special examinations, such as consultations, clinical laboratory, X-ray and other examinations; provisional or working diagnosis; medical or surgical treatment; gross and microscopical pathological findings; progress notes; final diagnosis; condition on discharge; follow-up; and autopsy findings.

The Department further directs that the record system conform with the recommendations of the Joint Commission on Accreditation of Hospitals.

b. *Retention:* There is a minimum 25 year retention period for all original or photographed records. Written approval of the Department of Health and Welfare is required before any records may be destroyed.

c. *Signature Requirements:* Regulation 2230 provides that all orders for medication and treatment must be written and signed by "one duly authorized to give such order within the State of New Hampshire."

New Jersey

a. *Creation and Contents:* The regulations are in the process of revision. The current regulations are contained in the *Manual of Standards for Private Hospitals,* Dept. of Institutions and Agencies (1952, reprinted 1965). Section seven lists the minimum requirements for medical records. Records must be "accurate and complete." They must be properly written and filed in an acceptable manner. Patients' records must include date of admission, provisional diagnosis, history, physical findings, physician's progress notes, record of operation and treatments, laboratory and x-ray reports, nurses' notes, consultations, physician's orders, final diagnosis and record of discharge.

b. *Retention:* Medical records must be completed within a reasonable time after the discharge of the patient. Records must be properly stored and retained for at least twenty-five years.

c. *Signature Requirements:* Section 6E requires that medication or treatment may only be given "on the order of a person authorized and professionally qualified to give such an order." While a signature is not specifically required, the implication is that one is needed.

e. *Confidentiality:* The confidential communications statute is quite comprehensive. In essence it provides for a privilege to prevent a witness from disclosing a communication, if the privilege is claimed and if the judge finds, among other things, that it was a confidential communication between patient and physician. The privilege applies to civil and criminal proceedings including juvenile delinquency matters. Exceptions to the privilege include actions contesting the validity of wills, actions where the condition of the patient is an element of the claim or defense, and reports to public officials. N.J. Stat. Ann. tit. 2A, §§84A-22.1 to -22.7 (Supp. 1970). The act appears to cover not only the physician but also those who are employed by the physician or those who learned of the communications as a result of a breach of the physician's duty of non-disclosure.

f. *Other Matters:* The hospital lien law provides that the hospital allow the party against whom the claim has been made to inspect the records. N.J. Stat. Ann. tit. 2A, §44-45 (1952).

New Mexico

a. *Creation and Contents: Rules, Regulations and Standards for Hospitals and Related Facilities,* Department of Public Health (1964), contain the record requirements.

Medical records must be written and kept for all patients and newborn infants. To be sufficient, a medical record must include identification data, complaint, relevant histories, physical examination, nursing notes, special examinations and reports, working diagnosis, medical, surgical and dental treatment, tissue reports, progress notes, final diagnosis, condition on discharge and follow-up. All orders must be written by the attending physician and included in the patient's medical record.

b. *Retention:* The retention provision makes reference to various statutes of limitations. It reads in part as follows:

> No time is fixed by law for the preservation of hospital records. However, records of adults may be needed to collect hospital bills within the six-year period for written contracts and four-year period for unwritten contracts, or for a three-year period to defend the hospital against personal injury claims, and it is desirable to retain records of children for one year after the child has attained the age of 21. The licensing

agency has no objection to microfilming of hospital records, provided that pertinent state statutes are not violated.

c. *Signature Requirements:* The order for discharge must be written in ink and signed by the attending physician or dentist or countersigned by him within twenty-four hours. Drugs and medications may not be given unless a signed written order has been made. Mechanical restraints may be imposed in a mental hospital only on a signed written order of the head of the hospital or his designee. N.Mex. Stats. §34-2-14 (1953)

e. *Confidentiality:* The confidential communications statute covers real or supposed venereal or loathsome disease or knowledge thereof obtained by examination. N.Mex. Stats. §20-1-12 (1953) The act applies to physicians, surgeons and professional or registered nurses.

New York

a. *Creation and Contents:* The State Hospital Code, promulgated by the State Hospital Review and Planning Council contains specific requirements for medical records. *Official Compilation of Codes, Rules and Regulations* tit. 10, ch. V, §720.20.

Section 720.20 provides that "accurate and complete medical records shall be written for all patients and filed in an easily accessible manner in the hospital." Items to be included in a complete medical record are identification data, dates of admission and discharge, complaints, the various histories, physical examination, doctor's orders including dietary orders, special examinations, provisional diagnosis, treatment and medications, surgical reports, progress notes, final diagnosis, condition at discharge, and autopsy findings, if performed.

b. *Retention:* Medical records, including those of the emergency room and outpatient department must be kept in the original form or reproduced "by any durable process acceptable to the commission which accurately reproduces the original." The records must be preserved for a period of not less than six years, or in the case of a minor, six years after majority. When records are reproduced, the original records may be destroyed. If a hospital discontinues operation, the governing authority (trustees, operator or public body) must maintain, store and service all medical records for not less than six years.

c. *Signature Requirements:* Orders for treatment or medication, must be written, signed in ink by the physician and filed in the patient's medical record. Reports filed in the record must be typewritten in ink and signed by the recording person. The record must be completed promptly, authenticated and signed by a physician or dentist within two weeks following discharge.

d. *Disclosure Authorized:* The regulation provides that procedures are to be established to govern release of information from a patient's medical record to respond to legitimate inquiries accompanied by duly signed authorizations. Staff use of records for research is to be governed by the written policy of the hospital.

e. *Confidentiality:* The confidential communications statute applies to civil and criminal procedures. It covers physicians, surgeons, dentists, registered or licensed practical nurses. The privilege is applicable to any information acquired in attending a patient in a professional capacity. Exceptions include information of a dentist for identification purposes, information about persons under 16 who may be victims of crime, information about the mental condition of the patient, or litigation involving the validity of wills where the interest of the personal representative are adverse to the deceased. N.Y. Civ. Prac. Act §4504 (Supp. 1970).

f. *Other Matters:* N.Y. Civ. Prac. Act §2306 (1963), authorizes the head of the hospital to send a certified transcript or reproduction of the record in response to a subpoena. Another section permits court ordered medical examinations and allows the parties to obtain copies of hospital records of such examinations.

The hospital lien law permits persons against whom a claim is asserted to examine the hospital records with reference to the treatment, care and maintenance of the injured person. The section excepts confidential communications or privileged records, unless the privilege is waived. N.Y. Lien Law §189 (1966).

Other provisions relating to information in the record are found in the Mental Hygiene Law, Public Health Law, Social Service Law and Workman's Compensation Law.

North Carolina

a. *Creation and Contents:* The requirements for medical records are specified in *Laws, Regulations and Procedures Applying to the Licensing of Hospitals in North Carolina,* Medical Care Commission, PART XIII (1964). All patients must have adequate and complete written records. The information contained in the records should "justify the diagnosis, verify the treatment and warrant the end results."

Those items specified to be contained in the record are identification data, dates for admission and discharge, personal and family history, chief complaint, history of present illness, physical examination, special examinations, provisional diagnosis, medical treatment, a complete surgical record, progress and nurses' notes, charts, final diagnosis, summary and condition on discharge.

b. *Retention:* Section E of the Regulations states that:

All original medical records or photographs of such records

shall be preserved or retained for at least the period outlined in the North Carolina Statute of Limitations and in accordance with hospital policy based on American Hospital Association recommendations and guidance of the hospital's legal advisors.

The medical record must be completed within a reasonable time after the discharge of the patient. The responsibility for completion is on the attending physician.

c. *Signature Requirements:* Records of medical treatment must be signed or initialed by the person giving the medication or treatment. Orders for medication and treatment are to be written in ink and signed by the prescribing physician. Verbal orders must be countersigned by the physician within twenty-four hours after they are given. Interpretations of electrocardiograms must be signed and made a part of the record. Radiology reports must also be signed by the physician responsible for the procedure.

The use of mechanical restraints in mental hospitals must be justified in the record and signed by the head of the hospital or his designee. When a surgical operation is to be performed on an inmate of a state institution, the chief medical officer and the medical staff of the institution must keep a careful and complete record of the measures taken to obtain consent and the complete medical record must be signed by the medical superintendent, the surgeon performing the operation and all surgical consultants, N.C. Gen. Stats. §130-191, (Repl. 1964).

North Dakota

a. *Creation and Contents:* The records requirements are contained in *Regulations and Standards for Hospitals and Related Institutions,* Dept. of Health (1956). The regulation provides that, at a minimum, the record must consist of identification data, dates of admission and discharge, physician's name, complete history and physical examination, graphic charts, working and final diagnosis, medication orders, progress notes, laboratory reports, nurses' notes, complete surgical record, and patient's condition when discharged. Records must also be kept on all newborns.

b. *Retention:* The regulation provides that provision shall be made for safe storage of all medical records in accordance with the statute of limitations.

c. *Signature Requirements:* The attending physician must include a signed report on the physical condition of a newborn immediately before the infant is discharged. The regulation states that accurate and complete medical records shall be written for all patients and signed by the attending physician. Orders for medication and treatment must be signed by the attending physician. Every use of a mechanical restraint in a mental hospital must be justified by a signed notation in the patient's record. N.D. Stat. §25-03-19.

d. *Disclosure Authorized:* Information relating to veterans may be released to them or to their personal representatives under conditions specified in N.D. Stat. §37-18-11.

e. *Confidentiality:* The confidential communications statute applies to physicians and surgeons and covers any information acquired in a professional capacity.

f. *Other Matters:* The hospital lien law permits any person against whom a claim is asserted to examine the records of the hospital which has filed a lien statement with reference to treatment, care and maintenance of an injured person.

Ohio

a. *Creation and Contents:* Regulations dealing with medical records are contained in *Ohio Sanitary Code,* 1968, adopted by the Public Health Council. Three chapters are directly applicable to hospitals, but none provides a specific delineation of what should be included in the medical record.

Chapter HE-13, Minimum Standards for Voluntary and Governmental Hospitals, Regulation 13 states that the medical record shall contain "sufficient data written in sequence of events to describe the basis for diagnosis and treatment of the patient concerned."

Chapter HE-9, Minimum Standards for Hospitals Receiving Federal Aid, provides:

HE-9-04 RECORDS AND REPORTS

(A) Records: Accurate and complete medical records shall be kept for all patients admitted to the hospital. These shall be filed in an accessible manner and each shall contain sufficient data to justify the diagnosis made and to warrant the treatment administered.

Chapter HE-7, Maternity Hospitals, Regulation 16, requires separate records for each maternity patient and each newborn infant. These records shall contain "sufficient data written in sequence of events to describe the basis for diagnosis and treatment of the patient concerned."

c. *Signature Requirements:* Of the three chapters cited above, only Chapter 7 on maternity hospitals offers guidelines on signature requirements. It would not be unreasonable to infer that the signatures required in maternity hospitals are likewise required in other kinds of hospitals.

All orders must be written in ink, dated and signed or countersigned by the attending physician. When a patient is discharged, the attending physician must signify approval by signing the medical record.

The use of restraints must be justified in writing in the patient's record and signed by the head of a mental hospital or a member of the medical staff pursuant to Ohio Rev. Code §5122.28 (1964).

e. *Confidentiality:* Pursuant to Ohio Rev. Code §2305.24 (Supp. 1969) utilization committee reports are confidential. The statute creates a right of action for the misuse of information by a member of the committee and it provides an immunity against liability for furnishing information to a utilization committee. The physician-patient privilege found at Ohio Rev. Code §2317.02 (1964) applies to communications made to the physician by the patient or the physician's advice to the patient, except that if the patient voluntarily testifies the physician may be compelled to testify on the same subject.

Oklahoma

a. *Creation and Contents:* The requirements for medical records are contained in *Standards and Regulations for Licensure of Hospitals and Related Institutions,* Department of Health (1967). Each medical record must be "accurate and complete." The records shall include identification data, medical history of current illness, physical examination, doctor's orders, progress notes, consultations, nurses' notes, diets, requests and results of clinical tests, and note of patient's condition when discharged. Complete records of surgery, obstetrical procedures and anesthesia are also required when applicable.

b. *Retention:* The regulations provide merely that microfilming of records, including X-ray reports, may be used to conserve storage space.

c. *Signature Requirements:* Orders for medication, treatment and tests must be written in ink and signed by the physician in charge. Signature stamps must not be used as a substitute for the signature of the authorizing doctor. All orders taken from the doctor, for entry by others, must be countersigned within 24 hours. Orders for emergency use of restraints must be signed by the physician as soon as possible.

d. *Disclosure Authorized:* Information may be disclosed for purposes of research and study by, among other groups, in-hospital staff committees. No liability will follow such disclosure.

e. *Confidentiality:* The confidential communications statute covers physicians and surgeons and applies to civil and criminal proceedings. Communications received in a professional capacity with reference to physical diseases and any knowledge obtained by personal examination are protected. Okla. Stat. Ann. tit. 12, §385 (1960).

Oregon

a. *Creation and Contents:* The *Rules, Regulations and Standards for Hospitals in Oregon,* Board of Health (1969) contain general requirements for the contents of medical records. However, the provisions relating to retention mention specific items which form part of the record.

b. *Retention:* The regulation contains a specific list which provides different time limits for separate items of the record. Included in this extensive list are: Case records or charts - twenty-five years from date of last discharge. Nurses' notes - five years. Electrocardiograms - five years. The regulations also provide that medical records, nurses' notes and X-rays which are no longer in use must be stored in the hospital and not disposed of except with written permission of the board.

Provision is made for microfilming with approval from the board of health.

c. *Signature Requirements:* The order for discharge must be written in ink and signed or countersigned by the attending physician. Records of newborn infants must contain a signed report by the attending physician on the infant's physical condition immediately before discharge. Ore. Rev. Stat. §426.385 provides that every use of mechanical restraints must be justified by a signed statement in the records of mental patients in state hospitals.

e. *Confidentiality:* The privileged communications statute applies to civil and criminal proceedings, covers physicians and surgeons and applies to any information acquired in a professional relationship. By statute, written notes, reports or records of tissue committees or other medical staff committees are inadmissible in evidence. Ore. Rev. Stat. §41-675.

f. *Other Matters:* A state statute requires medical records to be written in English:

Ore. Rev. Stat. §162.610

§162.610 RECORDS REQUIRED BY LAW TO BE IN ENGLISH.

(1) With the exception of druggists' or physicians' prescriptions, all records, reports and proceedings required to be kept by law shall be written in the English language or in a machine language capable of being converted to the English language by a data processing device or a computer.

* * *

A section of the Public Health Law permits any party legally liable or against whom a claim is asserted for compensation or damages for injuries to examine and make copies of all records of any hospital with reference to the hospitalization of the injured person. Ore. Rev. Stat. §441.510. Under the Insurance Law injured persons claiming compensation for injuries must execute an authorization to enable the insurer to obtain medical records and copies thereof.

Pennsylvania

a. *Creation and Contents:* The specific requirements for medical records are contained in *Rules and Regulations for Hospitals,* Department of Public Welfare (1966). Regulation 2144.1 specifies not only the requirements for in-patient records, but also the inclusions for emergency and out-patient records.

Medical records must be written for all in-patients. These records must be adequate and complete. The records must contain identification data, dates for admission and discharge, complaint, the various histories, physical examination, provisional diagnosis, temperature, pulse and respiration charts, examinations and reports, medical treatment, complete surgical record, progress notes, final diagnosis, discharge summary, and where applicable, autopsy findings.

All emergency or out-patients shall have written records that are adequate. The contents must include date of service, identification data, description of illness, treatment given or prescribed, and disposition of the patient.

b. *Retention:* Microfilming is approved for records over three years old. If records are not microfilmed they must be retained for not less than 15 years, after which time they may be destroyed provided a card file of pertinent information is maintained.

c. *Signature Requirements:* All records are to be legibly written by pen or typed and signed personally by the responsible physician. They must be authenticated and signed by a physician licensed in the state. Signed laboratory reports are to be in the patient's record. Signed radiographic reports are also to be in the patient's record.

e. *Confidentiality:* The privileged communications statute is restricted to civil proceedings and applies to physicians and surgeons. Pa. Stat. Ann. tit. 28 §328 (1958). It covers only information acquired in a professional capacity which may tend "to blacken the character" of the patient. Further exceptions include actions for personal injury.

Rhode Island

a. *Creation and Contents: General Regulations,* Department of Health - Division of Health Facilities (1966), contains a brief section on medical records:

PART IX - MEDICAL RECORDS

    37. The medical records shall be started for each patient at the time of admission. Admission notes by physician and

nurse shall be included. A complete history and physical examination of each patient shall be recorded by a physician within twenty-four (24) hours of admission and surgery, except in cases of unusual emergency.

c. *Signature Requirements:* Item 38 of the Regulations provides that the medical record must contain orders for medication and other services signed in ink by the prescribing physician. Radiological, clinical pathological and tissue reports must be signed and made part of the patient's record.

f. *Other Matters:* The hospital lien law allows persons against whom a claim has been asserted to examine the records of the hospital with reference to the claimed treatment, care and maintenance of the injured person. R.I. Gen. Laws §9-3-7. (Reenact. 1969)

A provision of a statute dealing with evidence permits defendants to subpoena records to refute claimed charges for medical and hospital services. R.I. Gen. Laws §9-19-27. (Reenact. 1969)

South Carolina

a. *Creation and Contents:* The medical record requirements appear in *Minimum Standards for Licensing in South Carolina Hospitals,* State Board of Health (1968).

Section 501.5 of the Standards requires that adequate and complete medical records be written for all patients admitted to the hospital. The minimum requirements include identification data, date of admission and discharge, history and physical examination, special examinations, provisional diagnosis, pre-operative diagnosis, treatment, complete surgical record, report of anesthesia, nurses' notes, progress notes, pathological findings, charts, final diagnosis, condition on discharge and autopsy findings in case of death.

b. *Retention:* Original records or photographs must be stored in the hospital and none may be disposed of under twenty-five years. If the hospital closes, the records must be kept intact. Hospitals that microfilm medical records before six years have elapsed must microfilm the entire medical record excluding nurses' notes, and may or may not maintain that part of the record not microfilmed. If records are microfilmed more than six years after they were originated, the governing body must decide the necessity of filming nurses' notes.

c. *Signature Requirements:* The standards require that all notes must be legibly written or typed and signed. Orders for restraints must be signed by the physician. Each attending physician must complete and sign the medical record within a period consistent with good medical practice. All medical records must contain orders for medication and treatment written in ink and signed by the prescribing physician. Verbal orders (given only to a RN or LPN) must be undersigned on the physician's next visit.

d. *Disclosure Authorized:* Records of patients in mental hospitals are confidential except that the patient, or his guardian, may consent if disclosure is necessary to carry out the provisions of the law. A court may order disclosure, or disclosure may be necessary for cooperation with state, federal and other agencies. S.C. Code §32-1022. (1962)

South Dakota

a. *Creation and Contents:* Hospital licensure requirements are contained in the *Regulations of the South Dakota State Department of Health,* Chapter Six.

Medical records must be accurate and complete. Items to be included are identification data, referral, admission date, physical examination, diagnosis, treatment, prognosis, nursing care, special reports and condition on discharge.

b. *Retention:* Regulation 6.3.6 requires that records be permanently retained for patients in general and specialized hospitals.

c. *Signature Requirements:* Regulation 6.2.10.3 requires that no medications or treatments shall be given except on the written order of a physician. The regulation requires all physicians' orders to be written in ink and signed. "Such orders shall be preserved on the patient's chart."

Regulation 6.3.6 requires the physician to enter the diagnosis on the patient's record at the time of admission, and also to record the patient's condition at the time of discharge.

e. *Confidentiality:* The confidential communications statute applies to physicians, surgeons or other practitioners of the healing arts; it covers any information acquired in a professional capacity and is applicable to both civil and criminal proceedings. S.D.C.L. §19-2-3 (1967).

Tennessee

a. *Creation and Contents:* The requirements for medical records appear in chapter 8 of *Minimum Standards and Regulations for Hospitals,* Department of Public Health (1966).

Regulation 801.4 requires "adequate and complete" medical records for all patients admitted to the hospital. Minimum contents of medical records include identification data, date of admission and discharge, physical examination and history, special examinations, provisional diagnosis, medical treatment, complete surgical record, anesthesia report, progress and nurses' notes, pathological findings, charts, final diagnosis, and condition on discharge.

b. *Retention:* Regulation 801.8 requires records and photographs to be confidential and stored in the hospital for a minimum of twenty-two years.

They cannot be disposed of except with the approval of the Hospital Licensing Board and the Department of Health. If a hospital closes, medical records may be disposed of as directed by the department.

c. *Signature Requirements:* The attending physician or dentist must complete and sign the medical record of each patient as soon as practicable after discharge. All medication and treatment orders must be written in ink and signed by the prescribing physician or dentist. If verbal orders are given they must be undersigned on the next visit. All notes are to be legibly written or typed and signed. Laboratory and X-ray reports are to be signed and placed in the patient's record. Orders for restraints must be signed by the physician.

d. *Disclosure Authorized:* Records may be routed to physicians for consultation. They may be made available for inspection by the Hospital Licensing Board of the Department.

e. *Confidentiality:* Records of patients in State Hospitals and those of patients receiving state financial assistance are confidential. They are subject to subpoena.

Texas

a. *Creation and Contents: Hospital Licensing Standards,* State Department of Health (Hospital Licensure Division, 1969) contains few clear references to medical records. There is no section specifically dealing with contents.

   Minimum Standards of Operation and Maintenance, (1948) promulgated by the Hospital Survey and Construction Division of the State Department of Health, applies to hospitals receiving Federal grants-in-aid. These standards provide that medical records must be accurate and complete. Minimum requirements include provisional diagnosis, history, physical findings, physician's progress notes, record of operation and treatment, special examinations and findings, nurses' notes, physician's orders, final diagnosis, and record of discharge or death.

b. *Retention: Hospital Licensing Standards* contains no reference to retention. *Minimum Standards of Operation and Maintenance* provides that records be kept for a period of at least 10 years. These records must be completed within a reasonable length of time after discharge of the patient.

c. *Signature Requirements: Hospital Licensing Standards* prohibit the giving of any medication or treatment except on the signed order of "one lawfully authorized to give such order." In emergencies the physician can give the order by telephone and sign it on his next visit. Radiological reports must "indicate" the individual who performed the tests.

d. *Disclosure Authorized:* Patient's records are confidential except that they may be disclosed with his consent or that of his guardian, to carry out provisions of the law by court order, or if the head of the hospital determines that disclosure is in the best interests of the patient. Disclosure of information as to the patient's current condition may be made to family, relatives and friends. Tex. Civ. Stat. Art. 5547 §87.

f. *Other Matters:* Persons against whom a claim for injuries has been filed may examine the record of the hospital with reference to the treatment, care and maintenance of the injured person. The hospital record may be admitted into evidence in any proceeding with respect to the recovery of damages. Tex. Civ. Stat. Art. 5506a §4a.

Utah

a. *Creation and Contents: Hospital Rules and Regulations,* State Division of Health (1968), contains an extensive section on medical records including a comprehensive authorization for the use of computers:

SECTION V

A. SERVICES AND FACILITIES

* * *

8. MEDICAL RECORD DEPARTMENT

* * *

Automated Record Systems-Nothing in these rules and regulations shall be construed to forbid the use of properly automated records or computerized orders provided:

(a) It contains proper patient identification.

(b) It contains adequate and sufficient data to establish diagnosis and describe the course and management of the individual patient.

(c) It provides proper physician identification and identification of any other person contributing to any part of the medical record.

(d) Consents for care and procedures and any release from liability from the patient must be signed and witnessed in the usual manner and kept on file.

Physician's orders may be given by computer, if such facilities are available and they meet the above requirements.

Medical records are required to be maintained for all patients. To be considered accurate and complete, the record must include identification

161

data, chief complaint, present illness, history and physical examination, provisional diagnosis, clinical laboratory and x-ray reports, consultations, medical and surgical treatment, tissue reports, progress notes, final diagnosis, and discharge summary.

b. *Retention:* Records must be kept for twenty-five years after the date of last discharge. However, nurses' notes must be maintained for at least seven years except those related to minor children which must be kept for one year after he reaches twenty-one. Prior to destroying any record a summary card must be prepared.

c. *Signature Requirements:* The attending physician must separately sign the history and physical examination, operative report, progress notes, drugs, medication, diet, and other orders for services and the summary. In hospitals with house officers, the attending physician must countersign at least the history and physical examination and the summary written by the house officer. A single signature on the face sheet of the record does not suffice to authenticate the entire content of the record. The original signed clinical laboratory report should be entered in the record. The original signed radiological report should also be entered. Use of restraints on mental patients must be justified by a signed order in the patient's record. Utah Code §64-7-48 (1953).

d. *Disclosure Authorized:* Authorized personnel may have access to records. Non-authorized personnel must gain access only with permission of the administrator or governing board. Division of Health Personnel may be permitted to review records as part of their compliance investigations. The patient must give written consent in order to authorize release of identifiable medical information.

e. *Confidentiality:* The privileged communications statute applies to physicians and surgeons and covers any information gained in the professional relationship. Utah Code §78-24-8 (1953)

Vermont

a. *Creation and Contents:* The licensing standards, promulgated by the State Department of Health in 1954, are in the process of revision.

The present standards require complete and accurate records for each patient admitted to the hospital. The records must include identification data, complaint, the various histories, physical examination, special examinations, working diagnosis, medical or surgical treatment, pathological findings, progress notes, final diagnosis, condition on discharge, follow-up, and autopsy findings. Medical records must be permanent, either typewritten or legibly written with pen and ink.

b. *Retention:* Records must be filed in a manner approved by the Department of Health and retained for at least 10 years.

c. *Signature Requirements:* No medication or treatment can be given except on the written order of a practicing physician. All medical records must be signed by the attending physician.

Virginia

a. *Creation and Contents: The Rules and Regulations Governing General and Special Hospitals,* Department of Health, adopted under Va. Code §32-301 (1947) provide scant information on medical records. The entire subject is covered by the following language:

> Records shall be made for all patients and filed in accessible manner with provision for their safe storage.

e. *Confidentiality:* The confidential communications statute applies to civil actions and covers duly licensed practitioners of any branch of the healing arts. Va. Code §8-289.1 (Supp. 1970) It relates to any information which the physician may have acquired in the professional relationship and the exceptions are the testimony as to the physical or mental condition or when the court in its sound discretion deems disclosure necessary.

f. *Other Matters:* A provision in the evidence code provides for the admission of copies or photographs of original medical records if they are properly authenticated by the custodian of the records.

Washington

a. *Creation and Contents: Hospital Rules and Regulations,* Department of Health (1968), contains specific record requirements as they appear in the Washington Administrative Code.

WAC 248-18-470 PATIENT'S BASIC MEDICAL RECORDS.

(1) The following minimum data shall be kept on all patients:

    a. Identifying and sociological data.

    b. Dates of admission and discharge.

    c. Medical history.

    d. Physical examination and findings.

    e. Medical orders.

    f. Progress notes.

    g. Summary report of patient's course in the hospital and condition on discharge.

h. Record of all medical care or treatments.

i. Reports of diagnostic procedures such as laboratory, X-ray, etc.

j. Nurse's record of care given to patients.

The regulations provide that an accurate and complete medical record shall be written for each patient.

c. *Signature Requirements:* Regulations require that the medical history, physical examination and findings, medical orders, progress notes, summary of patient's course in hospital and condition on discharge, and record of all medical care or treatment, are to be written, dictated or prepared by or under the supervision of the attending physician and signed by him.

e. *Confidentiality:* The confidential communications statute applies to regular physicians or surgeons with reference to any information required in attending the patient in the professional capacity. Wash. Rev. Code tit. 5 §5.60.060 It relates to civil and criminal matters. The privilege is qualified to the extent that it shall not apply in any judicial proceeding regarding a child's injuries, neglect or sexual abuse, or the cause thereof.

West Virginia

a. *Creation and Contents: West Virginia Regulations and Law for Licensing Hospitals,* State Department of Health (1969) contains the regulations for medical records at PART VI, Section C.

Regulation 603.1 requires accurate and complete written medical records on all patients.

603.1

b. A complete medical record is one which includes patient identification data, complaints, history of present illness, personal and family history, physical examination, doctor's orders including dietary orders, special examinations and consultations, clinical laboratory, X-ray and other examinations, provisional or working diagnosis, treatment and medications given, surgical reports including operative and anesthesia records, gross and microscopic pathological findings, progress notes, final diagnosis, condition on discharge, discharge summary and autopsy findings, if performed.

The same regulation provides for a "short form medical record" which may be used for patients staying in the hospital less than 48 hours. Maternity and newborn patients are excluded from this type of record. The short form need contain only sufficient information for proper diagnosis and treatment.

b. *Retention:* Regulation 603.1e provides that records "shall be preserved either in the original form or by microfilm or electronic data process." Since this is the only reference to retention, the implication is that records are to be permanently preserved.

Medical records must be completed promptly within 15 days but not more than 45 days following discharge of the patient.

c. *Signature Requirements:* All orders for medication or treatment are to be in writing and signed by the physician in ink. All orders, reports and entries are to be typewritten or written in ink and signed by the person making the entry. The records must be authenticated and signed by the physician or dentist.

e. *Confidentiality:* The physician-patient privilege applies to communications made to a physician in his professional capacity. W.Va. Code §50-6-10 (1966). It covers justices of the peace and constables. No statute has been found with reference to the testimony of physicians in courts of record.

Wisconsin

a. *Creation and Contents:* The *Rules of the Division of Health, General and Special Hospitals,* Department of Health and Social Services, (June, 1968) provide general and specific requirements for the contents of records including the requirement that all clinical information pertaining to the patient's stay shall be centralized in the patient's record. A specific reference to automation provides the following:

ADMINISTRATIVE RESPONSIBILITIES
* * *

(f) records shall be indexed according to disease, operation, and physician and shall be kept up-to-date. For indexing, any recognized system may be used.

* * *

3. In hospitals using automatic data processing, indexes may be kept on punch cards or reproduced on sheets kept in books. Wis. Adm. Code, ch. H 24 §24.07 (1968).

Pursuant to Wis. Stat. Ann. §51.075 (Supp. 1969) patients committed involuntarily to a state or county hospital have a right to evaluations from specified periods of time; the written evaluation must be placed in the patient's record.

b. *Retention:* The regulations provide that the hospital should have a writ-

165

ten policy for the preservation of medical records, either in the original or by microfilm, for a period of time determined by each hospital based on historical research, legal, teaching and patient care needs.

c. *Signature Requirements:* The regulations, in that portion relating to medical staff responsibilities, require signatures for reports of consultations. They also require that licensed practitioners must authenticate and sign records. Every physician must sign the entries he makes; a single signature on the face sheet is insufficient. In hospitals with a medical house staff, the attending physician shall countersign at least the history and physical examination and the summary written by a member of the house staff. Telephone orders must be signed or initialed by the physician within 24 hours. Nurses' notes shall be signed not initialed.

e. *Confidentiality:* The physician-patient privilege applies to information the physician may have acquired in attending the patient which was necessary to enable him to professionally serve the patient. Wis. Stat. Ann. § 885.21 (1958) This privilege does not apply to homicide trials, lunacy inquiries, civil or criminal malpractice cases, and any case where the patient consents.

d. *Disclosure Authorized:* The regulations provide that written consent of the patient shall be presented as authority for release of medical record information. A Wisconsin statute provides that upon written authorization and consent of the person who received medical care or treatment, or in the case of the patient's death, signed by his personal representative or beneficiary of a life insurance policy:

> (4) * * * the physician, surgeon or other person having custody of any medical or hospital reports, photographs, records, papers and writings concerning such care or treatment, shall forthwith permit the person designated in such authorization to inspect and copy such records. Any person having the custody of such records who refuses to comply with such authorization shall be liable to the person receiving such medical care and treatment for all reasonable and necessary costs of obtaining such copies and inspection and for attorney's fees not to exceed $50 plus costs. Wis. Stat. Ann. §269.57 (Supp. 1969).

This provision is not applicable to state or county mental hospitals, state colony and training schools or mental health clinics.

Wyoming

a. *Creation and Contents: Standards, Rules and Regulations for Hospitals,* Department of Public Health (1969), contains extensive medical record

166

requirements at section 14. Medical records must be maintained on all patients, and contain sufficient information to justify diagnosis and warrant the treatment and end results. The records shall include identification data, chief complaint, present illness, past and family history, physical examination, provisional diagnosis, clinical, laboratory and X-ray reports, consultations, medical and surgical treatment, progress notes, final diagnosis, discharge summary and autopsy findings.

b. *Retention:* Records shall be preserved either in the original or by microfilm, for a period of time not less than the statute of limitations. Tax supported hospitals must have the consent of the attorney general before destroying records.

Current records shall be completed within 24 to 48 hours following admission, while records of discharged patients must be completed within 15 days.

c. *Signature Requirements:* Consultation reports must be signed by the consultant. Radiological and laboratory reports must be signed. "Every physician shall sign or initial all entries which he himself makes." The regulation makes it clear that a single signature on the face sheet of the medical record shall not suffice to authenticate the entire record.

d. *Disclosure Authorized:* The records are to be kept confidential and only authorized personnel shall have access to them. Written consent of the patient must be presented for the release of medical information.

GLOSSARY OF LEGAL TERMS

Access Time: The time required for a processing component of a computer such as the Arithmetic Unit to receive or transmit data to the core storage component.

Administrative Agency: An arm of the government used to administer or carry out legislation. Example: State Health Department.

Admissibility (of evidence): Evidence that will be allowed to go to the jury according to the legal rules of evidence.

Affidavit: A sworn statement of facts or a declaration in writing and voluntarily made, that a person swears is true before a person with authority to administer an oath.

Agency: The relationship in which one person acts for or represents another, either as principal and agent, employer and employee or proprietor and independent contractor.

Alphanumeric: A generic term for alphabetic characters, numerical digits, and special characters which are machine readable, such as those represented in a punch card.

Analog Computer: A computer which represents variables or information by physical analogies (as contrasted with the digital computer), *i.e.,* an analog computer measures and a digital computer counts. An analog computer represents quantities or values by means of physical variables such as the rotational position of dials, or voltage or resistance in circuits.

Appellant: The party who appeals the decision of a lower court to an appellate court; usually the loser in the lower court.

Appellate Court: A court which has the power to review the actions of a lower court.

Appellee: The party against whom an appeal to an appellate court is taken; usually the winner in the lower court.

Arithmetic Unit: That component of the computer where arithmetic and logical operations are performed. It is usually contained in the same physical unit as core storage and the other processing components of a computer. See Central Processing Unit.

Assault: An intentional act designed to make the victim fearful and which produces in the victim reasonable apprehension of harm.

Battery: The nonconsensual touching of one person by another.

Best Evidence Rule: A legal doctrine that primary evidence of a fact such as an original document should be introduced, or its absence explained, before a copy or oral evidence on the same matter can be introduced.

Binary Coded Character: One element of the notation system for representing alphanumeric characters such as decimal digits, alphabetic letters and special characters, by a fixed code of binary digits.

Binary Digit: A digit or mark in the binary number system. Numeric

169

values in the binary number system are represented by only two digits, zero and one. The binary number system uses the equivalent of the decimal integer two as a base. For example, the decimal number 19 is represented by 10011 in the binary number system. Binary digits are commonly called "bits".

Bona Fide: In good faith; openly, honestly or innocently; without knowledge of fraud.

Borrowed Servant: An employee temporarily under the control of another. The traditional example is that of a nurse employed by a hospital who is "borrowed" by a surgeon in the operating room. The temporary employer of the borrowed servant will be held responsible for the act of the borrowed servant under the doctrine of *respondeat superior.*

Central Processing Unit (CPU): The central processor of the computer system, containing the main storage, arithmetic unit and logic circuits.

Civil Law: That part of American law which does not deal with crimes. Also, the law of countries such as Germany and France which follow the Roman Law system of jurisprudence in which most of the law is codified. (Compare common law.)

Common Law: That part of the law which is developed by means of decisions of the courts. It is distinguished from the statutory law as well as the civil law.

Computer: A device capable of accepting information, applying prescribed processes to the information, and supplying the results of these processes. It usually consists of input and output devices, storage, arithmetic, logical units, and a control unit.

Confidential Information: See Privileged Communication.

Consent: A voluntary act by which one person yields to another or agrees to allow someone else to do something. For medical and hospital procedures, consents should be in writing, with an explanation of the procedures to be performed, so that proof of consent is easy.

Console: A component of the computer which may be used to control the machine manually, correct errors, determine the status of machine circuits, registers, and counters, determine the contents of storage, and manually revise the contents of storage.

Control: (1) The part of a computer or processor which determines the execution and interpretation of instructions in proper sequence, including the decoding of each instruction and the application of the proper signals to the arithmetic unit and other registers in accordance with the decoded information. (2) Frequently, it is one or more of the components in any mechanism responsible for interpreting and carrying out manually-initiated directions. Sometimes it is called manual control. (3) In some business applications, a mathematical check. The control section of a computer is similar to a telephone exchange. It directs the operations of a computer according to a set of instructions called the program. These instructions are comparable to phone numbers dialed into a phone exchange which cause switches and controls to be activated.

Core Storage: (1) Pertaining to that component of a computer system in which data or information and program instructions can be stored and from which the computer can obtain at a later time those instructions or data values. The means of restoring data may be electrical or mechanical. Modern computers almost all use magnetic elements to store such information. (2) A device consisting of electronic or electrical hardware to which data may be entered and from which data may be obtained as required by the computer processing. (3) The erasable storage in any given computer. Synonymous with core, memory and storage.

Crime: An unlawful and prohibited act committed in violation of a penal statute. Crimes are prosecuted by and in the name of the state.

Criminal Law: The division of the law dealing with crime and punishment.

Data: A general term used to denote any or all facts, numbers, letters and symbols, or facts that refer to or describe an object, idea, condition, situation, or other factors. It connotes basic elements of information which can be processed or produced by a computer. Sometimes data is considered to be expressible only in numerical form, but information is not so limited.

Decedent: A deceased person.

Defamation: The injury of a person's reputation or character by willful and malicious statements. Defamation includes both libel and slander.

Defendant: In a criminal case, the defendant is the person accused of committing a crime. In a civil suit, the defendant is the party against whom suit is brought seeking damages or other legal relief.

Deposition: A sworn statement of facts made out of court which may be admitted into evidence if the attendance of the witness is not possible.

Digital Computer: A computer which uses integral numbers in a given base to represent all the quantities that occur in a problem or a calculation. It is possible to express in digital form all information stored, transferred, or processed as well as the instructions to do the processing by a dual state condition; *e.g.,* on-off, open-closed, and true-false. The digital computer is more versatile than an analog computer. It is the most common type of computer.

Direct Access: (1) A storage concept in which the time required to access information is independent of the location of the information most recently obtained. (2) A type of storage in which access can be made directly to any storage location regardless of its position, either absolute or relative to the previously referenced information. Contemporary direct access de-

171

vices are disk and drum storage units. See serial access. Synonymous with direct access storage or direct access device.

Directed Verdict: A decision of the judge that the evidence or law is so clearly in favor of one party that it is pointless to proceed further with the trial, whereupon the judge directs the jury to return a verdict for that side.

Discovery: Pre-trial activities of attorneys to determine what evidence the opposing side will present if the case comes to trial. Discovery serves to prevent attorneys being surprised during trial and to facilitate out-of-court settlement. Since discovery is a variance from the way cases are usually tried, the rules for its use are very strict.

Disk: A storage device on which information is recorded on the magnetizable surface of a rotating disk. A magnetic disk storage system is an array of such devices, with associated reading and writing heads which are mounted on movable arms.

Drum: A cylinder having a surface coating of magnetic material, which stores binary information by the placement of opposite magnetic charges, called dipoles, near or in its surface. Since the drum is rotated at a uniform rate, the information stored is available periodically as a given portion of the surface moves past one or more detecting devices called read/write heads located near the surface of the drum.

Emergency: A sudden unexpected occurrence, an unforeseen event or condition causing a threat to life or health. The legal responsibilities of those involved in an emergency situation are measured in light of the occurrence.

Employee: One who works for another, the employer. The latter selects and employs the person, pays him a salary or wages, retains the power to dismiss him, and can control his conduct during working hours.

Employer: See Employee.

Encode: (1) To apply a code, frequently one consisting of binary numbers, to represent individual characters or groups of characters in a message. Synonymous with encipher. Inverse of decode. (2) To substitute letters, numbers, or characters for other numbers, letters, or characters.

Equity Practice: That part of the law which deals with situations where there is no legal remedy or where awaiting the decision of the court would work too great a hardship on the party seeking relief. Among other things courts of equity grant injunctions, and secure title to specific property. Equity and law courts are now merged in many places. (Compare common law.)

Expert Witness: One who has special training, experience, skill, and knowledge in a relevant area, and who is allowed to offer opinion testimony in court.

Felony: A crime of a serious nature usually punishable by imprisonment for a period of longer than one year.

Good Samaritan Law: A statute designed to protect those who stop to render aid in an emergency.

Hard Copy: A printed copy of machine output; *e.g.*, printed reports, listings, documents, and summaries.

Hardware: The mechanical, magnetic, electrical and electronic devices or components of a computer system. See software.

Hearsay Rule: A rule of evidence that restricts the admissibility of evidence not coming from the personal knowledge of the witness. Hearsay evidence is admissible in certain circumstances under strict rules.

In Loco Parentis: A legal doctrine which provides that under certain circumstances a person, assigned by the court, may stand in the place of parents and possesses their legal rights, duties, and responsibilities.

Independent Contractor: One who agrees to undertake work by his own method and means, without being under the control or direction of the employer, except perhaps incidentally.

Indictment: A formal written accusation of crime brought by the prosecuting attorney against one charged with criminal conduct.

Injunction: An equitable remedy requiring one to do or to refrain from doing certain acts.

Input: (1) Information or data transferred or to be transferred from outside the computer into the internal storage of the computer; (2) Describing the routines which direct input or the devices from which such information is made available to the computer; (3) The device or collective set of devices necessary for input.

Instruction: A set of identifying characters or binary codes designed to cause a computer to perform certain operations. A machine instruction usually consists of one or more operator codes, operands or addresses. The operators define the function to be performed. The operands or addresses specify the location of the information upon which the operation is to perform or the location where the result is to be stored.

Interface: A common boundary between two systems or two devices or two components within a system.

Judge: An official who controls court proceedings to insure impartiality and who sees that the rules of evidence are observed. The trial judge determines the applicable law and explains it to the jury which applies the law to the facts it has found. The appellate judge hears appeals and renders decisions about the actions of the trial judge, the law of the case and the sufficiency of the evidence.

Jurisprudence: The philosophy or science of law upon which a particular legal system is built.

Jury: A certain number of persons who are selected and sworn to hear the evidence and determine the facts in a case.

Liability: An obligation one has incurred or might incur through any act or failure to act.

Liability Insurance: A contract to have another indemnify or pay for any liability or loss thereby in return for the payment of premiums.

Libel: A false or malicious writing intended to defame or dishonor another person, which is published or presented so that someone besides the one defamed will see it.

License: A permit from the state giving one permission to perform certain acts, usually for a specific period of time.

Lien: A remedy of a creditor to secure an interest in property of the debtor in satisfaction of his debt.

Litigation: A trial or proceeding in court to determine legal issues and rights and duties between the parties to the trial.

Malpractice: Professional negligence resulting from improper discharge of professional duties or failure to meet the standard of care of a professional, which results in harm to another.

Multiple Access: Parallel (1) To handle simultaneously in separate facilities; (2) To operate on two or more parts of a word or item simultaneously. Contrasted with serial.

Negligence: Carelessness, failing to act as an ordinary prudent person, or acting in a way contrary to what a reasonable person would have done.

Next of Kin: Those people who by the law of descent would be the closest blood relatives of the decedent, such as the parents of a child, or the brother or sister of an orphan.

Notary Public: A public official who administers oaths and certifies the validity of documents.

Off-Line: Descriptive of a system and of the peripheral equipment or devices in a system in which the operation of peripheral equipment is not under the control of the central processing unit.

On-Line: Descriptive of a system and of the peripheral equipment or devices in a system in which the operation of such equipment is under control of the central processing unit, and in which information reflecting current activity is introduced into the data processing system as soon as it occurs. Thus, directly in-line with the main flow of transaction processing.

Operator: (1) A mathematical symbol which represents a mathematical process to be performed on the data involved in a computer operation. (2) The portion of an instruction which tells the machine what to do. (3) A person who operates a machine.

Opinion of the Court: In an appellate court decision, the reasons for the decision will be stated. One judge will write the opinion for the majority of the court. Judges who agree with the result but for different reasons may write concurring opinions explaining their reasons. Judges who disagree with the majority may write dissenting opinions.

Ordinance: A law passed by a municipal legislative body, *i.e.,* city council.

Output: (1) The information transferred from the internal storage of a computer to the outside storage, or to any device outside of the computer. (2) The device or collective set of devices necessary to make the transfer. (3) To transfer from internal storage on to external media.

Perjury: The willful act of giving false testimony under oath.

Plaintiff: The party to a civil suit who brings the suit seeking damages or other legal relief.

Police Power: The power of the state to protect the health, safety, morals, and general welfare of the people.

Prima Facie: "At first sight," or presumably. A thing is presumed true unless it is disproved by contrary evidence.

Privileged Communication: Statements made to one in a position of trust such as to an attorney, physician, or spouse. Because of the confidential nature of such information, the law protects it from being revealed, even in court. The term is applied in two distinct situations. First, the communications between certain persons, *e.g.,* physician and patient, cannot be divulged without consent of the patient. Second, in some situations the law provides an exemption from liability for disclosing information where there is a higher duty to speak. Example: Statutory reporting requirements.

Probate: The judicial proceeding which determines the existence and validity of a will.

Probate Court: Courts with jurisdiction over wills. Their powers range from deciding the validity of a will, to the distribution of property thereunder.

Processing Data: (1) The preparation of source media which contain data or basic elements of information, and the handling of such data according to precise rules of procedure to accomplish such operations as classifying, sorting, calculating, summarizing, and recording. (2) The production of records and reports. Synonymous with data handling.

Program: (1) The complete plan for the solution of a problem, more specifically the complete sequence of machine instructions and routines necessary to solve a problem. (2) To plan the procedure for solving a problem. This may involve among other things the analysis of the problem, preparation of a flow diagram, preparing details, testing, and developing subroutines, allocation of storage locations, specification of input and output formats, and the incorporation of a computer run into a complete data processing system. Related to routine.

Punch Card: A card in which punches in designated locations represent data which can be conveyed to other machines or devices by reading or sensing the holes. Synonymous with Hollerith card.

Real Time: Concurrent data processing operations within the computer itself and the external physical processing in such a way that the results of the computer's operations are available whenever needed by the physical processing operations, and vice versa. An airline reservation system is an example of a real time computer system.

Rebuttal: The giving of evidence to contradict the effect of evidence introduced by the other side.

Regulatory Agency: An arm of the government empowered to carry out legislation which regulates an act or activity in a particular area. Example: The Federal Food and Drug Administration.

Release: A signed statement by one giving up a right or claim against another, usually done for consideration or money.

Remote Access: Pertaining to the ability to obtain data from or place data in a storage device or register directly without serial delay due to other units of data, and usually in a relatively short period of time.

Res Gestae: "Things happening." All of the events which become part of an incident. If statements are made as part of the incident they are admissible in court as *res gestae,* in spite of the hearsay rule.

Res Ipsa Loquitur: "The thing speaks for itself." A doctrine of law that applies to cases where the harm which occurred would not ordinarily have happened without negligence and where the defendant had exclusive control of the instrument causing the harm. A presumption is raised which the defendant has the burden to rebut.

Respondeat Superior: "Let the master answer." The employer is responsible for the legal consequences of the acts of the servant or employee while he is acting within the scope of his employment.

Retrieval: The recovering of desired information or data from a collection of documents or other graphic records.

Routine: A set of coded instructions arranged in proper sequence to direct the computer to perform a desired operation or sequence of operations. A subdivision of a program consisting of two or more instructions that are functionally related; therefore, a program. Related to program.

Serial: The handling of one item or element after the other in a single facility, such as transfer or storage in a digit-by-digit time sequence, or to process a sequence of instructions one at a time, *i.e.,* sequentially as contrasted with parallel.

Serial Access: A data access technique in which the transfer of data elements is successive—that is in sequence, one after the other. To access a particular data element in a serial access process requires the access of all data elements preceding the target data element. Magnetic tape devices are the most common form of serial access device.

Shop Book Rule: If books are kept in the usual course of business they may be introduced in court despite the hearsay rule, so long as they are properly authenticated and held in proper custody.

Slander: An oral statement made with intent to dishonor or defame another person when made in the presence of a third person.

Software: That part of a complete computer system which is not hardware. Specifically, the programs and the system procedures as stored and processed by the computer. See hardware.

Standard of Care: Those acts performed or omitted that an ordinary prudent person or an ordinary person with training would have done or not done. A measure against which the defendant's conduct is compared.

Stare Decisis: "Let the decision stand." The legal principle that courts should follow previous decisions and apply them to subsequent cases involving similar facts and questions.

State Statute, Statutory Law: A declaration of the legislative branch of government having the force of law.

Statute of Limitations: A legal limit on the time one has to file suit in civil matters, usually measured from the time of the injury or from the time that a reasonable man would have discovered the injury.

Subpoena: A court order requiring one to come to court to give testimony.

Subpoena Duces Tecum: A subpoena that commands a person to come to court and to bring with him the documents named in the order.

Suit: Court proceeding where one person seeks damages or other legal remedies from another. The term is not usually used in connection with criminal cases.

Summons: A court order telling the sheriff to notify the defendant in a civil suit that suit has been filed against him, and telling him when and where to appear.

Time Sharing: The use of a computer by two or more processes during the same overall time interval, accomplished by interspersing component actions in time. Usually involves accessing a computer's resources by remote consoles.

Tort: A civil wrong. Torts may be intentional or unintentional.

Tortfeasor: One who commits a tort.

Trial Court: The original court in which the evidence is presented to the judge or jury for decision.

Uniform Act: An act concerning a particular area of the law, such as business records as evidence, which is created by a non-legal body, such as the National Conference of Commissioners on Uniform State Laws, with the hope that it will be enacted in all the states so as to maintain a uniformity of law in a particular area.

Verdict: The formal declaration of the jury of its findings of fact, which is signed by the jury foreman and presented to the court.

Voice Grade: Refers to a communications channel which permits the transmission of speech. Ordinary telephone lines used for voice communication as well as teletype class communications are called voice grade channels or low-level data transmission channels. Voice grade channels are most commonly used for the communication network in time-sharing or real time system applications.

Waiver: The intentional giving up of a right that one knows he possesses, such as allowing another to testify to information that would ordinarily be protected as a privileged communication.

Witness: One who is called to give testimony in a court of law.

Written Authorization: Consent given in writing specifically empowering someone to do something.